P9-BBO-442

Step-By-Step
Repair Manual

It doesn't necessarily take a highly trained service technician to make most repairs on an appliance. This book shows you just how easy it can be to repair your own dryer. Whether you're an avid do-it-yourselfer or just a beginner, the step-by-step photo instructions and detailed explanations will help you to perform the majority of dryer repairs you're likely to encounter.

By learning to do as many of your own repairs as possible, you save time and money.

Safety Information: Electric and gas dryers are complex electromechanical appliances. Any attempt to repair your dryer may, if improperly performed, result in personal injury and property damage. GE cannot be responsible for the interpretation of this manual, nor can it assume any liability in connection with its use. For more detailed safety information see page 2 of this manual.

If your appliance is still under warranty: Before you attempt any repairs, check to see if your appliance is covered under warranty. If you or any unauthorized service technician tries to repair an appliance under warranty, the warranty may be voided.

Step-by-Step Repair Manual for GE/Hotpoint
Dryers
General Electric Company

©1990 by General Electric Co.
    Appliance Park
    Louisville, KY 40225

Contents

Note: Pages 1 through 7 contain important information. Be sure to carefully read these pages before you begin any repair procedures.

How to use this manual

GE has recognized the growing need for the homeowner to perform as many of the service operations as possible around the house. Consequently, we have prepared this manual to provide the typical homeowner with the information necessary to perform the majority of dryer repairs. This manual is written in an easy to follow, step-by-step, photo guide format to instruct you how to do your own repairs.

Before you begin your repair

It is important that before you begin any repair or diagnosis on your dryer you take the time to read the general information on pages 2 thru 7. By acquiring a basic understanding of dryer repair and important safety information, you'll be a step ahead on diagnosing and remedying the problem.

Problem Diagnostic Charts

When a problem does occur, refer to the Problem Diagnostic Chart section of the manual (pages 7-11). These charts will help you pinpoint your trouble by listing possible causes from the most likely to the least common cause. The charts will refer you to the repair procedures (pages 12-84) that use photography and illustrations to show you step-by-step how to remedy the problem. Be sure to read the entire repair procedure carefully before attempting any work.

Glossary of Terms

If you find a term you don't understand, you may find it listed in the Glossary of Terms (pages 94-97). Also, don't forget to use the index in the back of this manual as a reference when searching for various information.

Read your *Use and Care Book*

After you have read the introductory sections in this manual, you may want to re-read the **Use and Care Book** that accompanies your dryer. The **Use and Care Book** can tell you how to remedy many problems that aren't due to equipment failures, such as overloading and lint accumulation. You may just discover that your dryer has useful features you've forgotten.

Preventive Maintenance

When you have completed your repair, the Preventive Maintenance section (page 86) can help you obtain the best results from your GE or Hotpoint dryer. Preventive maintenance is a vital key to long life for your dryer. The few minutes you invest in caring for your dryer properly can save you a great deal of time and trouble.

What repairs are covered?

Although GE has introduced hundreds of dryer models through the years, similarities in basic components allow this manual to cover most common repairs. Some procedures may not apply to your dryer; they may be applicable only for a particular brand (GE or Hotpoint), or model type. For instance, your model will have either electric heaters or a gas combustion chamber, but it will not have both. The component being repaired may also vary in location or design with different dryer models. Major differences between models will be noted in the repair procedure.

Safety information

Dryers are complex electromechanical appliances. Any attempt to repair your dryer may, if improperly performed, result in personal injury and property damage. GE cannot be responsible for the interpretation of this manual, nor can it assume any liability in connection with its use.

Safety Precautions
To minimize the risk of personal injury or property damage it is important that the following safe practices be observed:

---

1. **Be sure that you are operating your dryer properly. Read carefully the** *Use and Care Book* **that comes with your dryer.**

2. **Know the location of your dryer's circuit breakers or fuses. Clearly mark all switches and fuses for quick reference. If you are unfamiliar with circuit breakers and fuses, please refer to Procedure #1: Inspecting Circuit Breakers and Fuses.**

3. **Before servicing your dryer turn off controls. Disconnect the power supply at the distribution panel by removing the fuse or switching off the circuit breaker. UNPLUG the power cord before performing any repairs or removing any access panel. Note: Except for Procedures #17 and #18, which refer to dryer gas assemblies, none of the repairs in this manual require voltage to be applied to the dryer during the repair procedure.**

4. **Be careful when handling access panels, dryer parts, or any components that may have sharp edges. Avoid placing your hand into any areas of the dryer that you cannot first visually inspect for sharp edges.**

5. **Do not light a match around the gas burner. If you smell gas, open windows, extinguish any open flames, don't touch electrical switches, and call your gas supplier.**

6. **Never interfere with or bypass the operation of any switch, component, or feature of the dryer.**

7. **Use only replacement parts of the same size and capacity as the original part. If you have any question contact your authorized local appliance parts dealer.**

8. **Before reconnecting the power supply, make sure that no uninsulated wires or terminals are touching the cabinet. Electrical wiring and grounds must be correctly reconnected and secured away from sharp edges, high temperature components, and moving parts. All panels and covers should be reinstalled before the dryer is plugged in.**

9. **The internal wiring of dryers is made with special heat-resistant insulation. Therefore, ordinary wire must never be substituted. Since the wire carries heavy currents and is subjected to heat, it is especially important that all connections are tight and secure.**

10. **Exhaust ductwork should be the specified size and material suited for dryers. The ductwork must be placed in position to vent air to the outside before operating your dryer. The total length and number of turns should be kept to a minimum. Refer to installation instructions that come with your dryer.**

11. **If moved out from the wall, the dryer should be checked when pushed back into position to insure that it is level and that ductwork is in place and not kinked. The legs should be securely locked into position.**

12. **Carefully read through the entire repair procedure for a specific repair before attempting the job. If you don't fully understand the repair procedure or doubt your ability to complete it, call a qualified service technician.**

13. **Throughout this manual additional safety precautions dealing with specific repair procedures will be presented. This information should be read carefully.**

Parts information

Obtaining replacement parts

If you're going to the time and trouble of repairing your appliance, it is important that you get the correct replacement part. First, be sure you have the complete model number for your appliance when ordering replacement parts. Even if you take in the original part, a salesperson may not be able to supply the correct replacement part without your complete model number. Second, to assure proper fit and performance, use Genuine GE Renewal Parts.

The model specification plate is mounted on the upper right side of the dryer front, inside the dryer door.

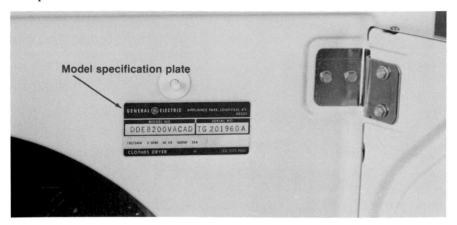

GE dryer specification plate

Hotpoint dryer specification plate

Finding your model number

The model and serial numbers of your dryer are stamped on a metal model specification plate. On most GE/Hotpoint dryers, you will find the model specification plate inside the dryer door near the top right hinge.

The complete model number must be used when ordering exact replacement parts. Be sure to copy this number correctly and record it on page 85 of this manual for future reference.

Genuine GE Renewal Parts

All parts are not created equal when it comes to your GE or Hotpoint dryer. Some non-GE parts may require extra brackets and adapters to make them fit. Others may not be designed for the exact electrical specifications of your dryer and, as a result, may cause substandard performance. With Genuine GE Renewal Parts you are assured a proper fit and performance match for the original part – an assurance that's backed in writing with a one-year limited warranty.

For your convenience in obtaining parts, GE has company-owned parts stores and authorized dealers throughout the country. To find the outlet nearest you, look in the Yellow Pages under major headings, "Appliances--Household--Major" or "Dryers", then subheads, "Service & Repair" or "Supplies & Parts". If you are unable to find where GE parts are sold in your area, call the GE Answer Center® consumer information service toll free number (1-800-626-2000) for assistance.

Genuine GE Renewal Parts are backed by a one-year limited warranty to assure you proper fit and performance.

Some dealers feature the Quick Fix® system of common GE replacement parts and parts kits. Designed specifically for do-it-yourselfers, Quick-Fix® parts come in clearly marked packages complete with hardware and step-by-step replacement instructions.

Whether it's the Quick-Fix® system or the regular GE line of parts, you should insist on the performance and quality of Genuine GE Renewal Parts. After all, if you're investing time and money to care for your appliance, it's better to do it right the first time and not chance problems later from using an unsuitable part.

4

How your dryer operates

The more you know about the mechanical and electrical operation of your dryer, the easier it will be to understand the causes and solutions to a problem. For example, when you use your dryer, you load it with clothes, set a timer or automatic control, and activate the start button. But what causes the clothes to tumble, and how does heated air flow to the clothes? Answers to these questions could make it easier for you to repair your dryer. So let's take a closer look at how your dryer operates.

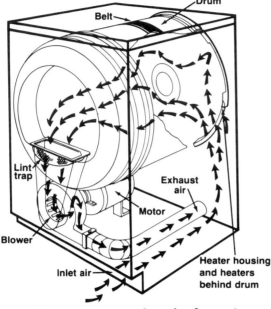

Type A (some electric dryers)

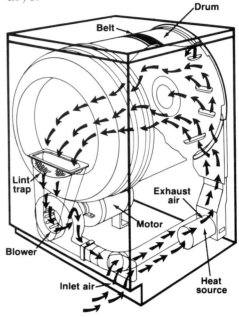

Type B (gas and some large capacity electric dryers)

It all starts at the power supply cord that connects your dryer to the electrical outlet (receptacle). Large, flexible wires within the cord carry the power to the dryer's internal wiring network, where power is distributed to various parts of the control system. The control system consists of a series of switches and thermostats, which turn the heating source and motor on and off.

All dryers, whether gas or electric, operate according to the same principle — they remove moisture from damp clothes by bringing the clothes in contact with a flow of heated air. Mechanically, the clothes must tumble to expose all of their surfaces to heat, and the heated air must be circulated within the dryer and vented.

Switches, timers, and thermostats regulate the air temperature and duration of the drying cycle.

When the start button is activated with the dryer door closed, electrical power is sent to start a motor. The motor is connected to the drum by a drive belt. The drive belt rotates the drum through a pulley system attached to the motor shaft. The drum itself is supported by a bearing at the rear and Teflon® slides at the front.

The blower pulls incoming air through the heat source into the drum and pushes moist air from the dryer through the ductwork to the outside vent. Air circulation is important for the dryer to maintain the proper air temperature.

In electric dryers, the heat source is not energized until the drive motor starts turning. Both the timer and thermostats energize coiled resistance heaters. The temperature selector switches control the number of heaters energized.

In gas dryers, the heat source is from a gas burner. For safety reasons, the gas must pass through two valves before reaching the opening where it is ignited. The flow of gas is controlled by a pressure regulator. The safety valve is held open through an electrical circuit. If the voltage is cut off (as it would be, for example, if the dryer door were opened), the gas flow would be turned off automatically.

5

Models covered

Over the years, GE/Hotpoint has produced hundreds of various dryer models. Repairs on most models are similar, so most problems that may arise with your dryer are likely to be covered in this manual.

Exception: This manual does not cover repairs for compact, portable dryers (dryers less than 27″ wide).

Standard capacity dryer is available with a variety of heat and fabric settings and shut-off controls to dry average-size wash loads.

Standard capacity gas dryer uses natural gas as the energy source rather than 220-volt electricity. Popular in areas that heavily use natural gas, this dryer is equipped with similar drying options and convenience features found on electric models.

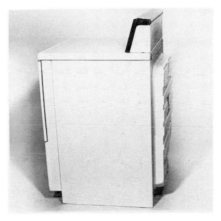

Large capacity electric dryer is equipped to handle larger, family-size wash loads. Models vary in the number of heat selections offered for specific fabric types and in shut-off controls.

A more recent large capacity electric dryer has the same size opening as the standard capacity dryer, but extra space out the back of the dryer. Care must be taken not to push this model tightly against the wall.

Problem diagnostic charts

How to use the problem diagnostic charts

The problem diagnostic charts help you with one of the most difficult tasks in do-it-yourself repairs...locating the possible causes and solutions to your problem. Before using the charts, make note of the problem you are experiencing with your dryer. Keen observation can often lead you to the area where the problem lies. Watch for anything that deviates from normal operation. Note everything that is or is not working. Once you have identified a problem, then you can begin to solve it by referring to the Problem Diagnostic Charts.

Each page of the Problem Diagnostic Charts has four columns of information: (1) **Problem;** (2) **Possible Cause;** (3) **Repair Procedure;** and (4) **Skill Level.** The first column, **Problem**, lists examples of the problems you may encounter with your dryer, In the second column, there is a list of **Possible Causes** that may be the reason for the problem. The possible causes for each problem are listed in the order in which they might be expected to occur, from the most likely to the least likely. A **Repair Procedure** for each possible cause is listed in column three. Repair procedure information refers you to a course of action to remedy the possible cause of your dryer problem.

The final column, **Skill Level**, indicates a skill level rating for each repair task. This rating will help you decide which repairs you feel confident of completing.

●	Easy	No previous experience needed
● ●	Average	Requires removal of service panels. Mechanical ability is helpful
● ● ●	Difficult	May require the use of an ohmmeter and/or splicing of electrical wires. Repair or replacement of component parts is more difficult.
● ● ● ●	Very Difficult	May require the use of an ohmmeter and the ability to read a circuit diagram. Repair or replacement of component parts is complex.
● ● ● ● ●	Requires Service Technician	Requires special tools and skills

No matter what skill level assigned to a task, study the repair procedure and safety instructions carefully before proceeding.

NOTE:
The problems listed below are numbered exactly as they appear in the PROBLEM column of the Problem Diagnostic Charts.

Dryer problems

1. Dryer will not run
2. Motor runs, but dryer will not heat
3. Dryer will not turn off
4. Dryer stops during cycle
5. Clothes overheat
6. Clothes do not dry or drying time too long (electric dryer)
7. Clothes do not dry or drying time too long (gas dryer)
8. Dryer is noisy
9. Dryer runs with door open
10. Dryer drum does not rotate, but motor runs
11. Damaged dryer body

Problem diagnostic charts

Problem	Possible Cause	Repair Procedure	Skill Level
1. Dryer will not run	No power to dryer (blown fuse or tripped breaker)	Check Power Supply (See p.13 & Procedure #1)	•
	Terminal block inoperative	Check Terminal Block (See p.25 & Procedure #6)	••
	Centrifugal switch inoperative	Check Centrifugal Switch (See p.71 & Procedure #21)	•••
	Motor winding burned out	Check Motor (See p.73 & Procedure #22)	••••
	Open contact in timer	Check Timer (See p.33 & Procedure #10)	••••
	Open contact in door switch	Check Door Switch (See p.81 & Procedure #26)	•••
	Power cord defective	Check Power Cord (See p.17 & Procedure #3)	•••
	Start switch inoperative	Check Start Switch (See p.31 & Procedure #9)	••••
	Door is open	Check Door Alignment (See p.79 & Procedure #24)	••
		Check Door Latch (See p.80 & Procedure #25)	••
2. Motor runs, but dryer does not heat	Dryer set on fluff cycle	See *Use and Care Book*	
	Blown fuse or tripped breaker in 1 side of power line to dryer	Check Power Supply (See p.13 & Procedure #1)	•
	Open electric heating element (electric dryers only)	Check Electric Heater Coils (See p.53 & Procedure #16)	••••
	Centrifugal switch inoperative	Check Centrifugal Switch (See p.71 & Procedure #21)	•••
	Open contact in timer	Check Timer (See p.33 & Procedure #10)	••••
	Thermostat(s) inoperative	Check Thermostats – Electric Dryers (See p.41 & Procedure #13)	•••
		Check Thermostats – Gas Dryers (See p.45 & Procedure #14)	•••
	Gas burner inoperative (gas dryers only)	Check Gas Assembly (See p.57 & Procedure #17) or (See p.61 & Procedure #18)	••••
	Corroded terminal at heating element (electric dryers only)	Check Electric Heater Coils (See p.53 & Procedure #16)	••••
	Incorrect voltage at terminal block	CALL SERVICE TECHNICIAN	•••••
	Open contact in selector switch	Check Selector Switches (See p.20 & Procedure #8)	••••

Skill Level Index: • Easy •• Average ••• Difficult •••• Very Difficult ••••• Requires Service Technician

8

Problem diagnostic charts (continued)

Problem	Possible Cause	Repair Procedure	Skill Level
3. Dryer will not turn off	Thermostat(s) inoperative	Check Thermostats – Electric Dryers (See p.41 & Procedure #13)	•••
		Check Thermostats – Gas Dryers (See p.45 & Procedure #14)	•••
	Timer inoperative	Check Timer (See p.33 & Procedure #10)	••••
	Resistor inoperative (electric dryers only)	Check Resistor (See p.35 & Procedure #11)	•••
	Cold room	Room temperature must be 50°F or more	
	Moisture sensor inoperative	Check Moisture Sensor (See p.49 & Procedure #15)	•••
4. Dryer stops during cycle	Interruption of power supply	Check Power Supply (See p.13 & Procedure #1)	•
	Motor overheating	Check Motor (See p.73 & Procedure #22)	••••
	Timer inoperative	Check Timer (See p.33 & Procedure #10)	••••
5. Clothes overheat	Improper vent installation	Check Dryer Vent (See p.15 & Procedure #2)	•
	Grounded heating element (electric dryers only)	Check Electric Heater Coils (See p.53 & Procedure #16)	••••
	Thermostat(s) inoperative	Check Thermostats – Electric Dryers (See p.41 & Procedure #13)	•••
		Check Thermostats – Gas Dryers (See p.45 & Procedure #14)	•••

Skill Level Index: •Easy ••Average •••Difficult ••••Very Difficult •••••Requires Service Technician

Problem	Possible Cause	Repair Procedure	Skill Level
6. Clothes do not dry or drying time is too long (electric dryers)	Improper vent installation	Check Dryer Vent (See p.15 & Procedure #2)	•
	Heating system inoperative	Check Electric Heater Coils (See p.53 & Procedure #16)	••••
	Timer improperly set	See *Use and Care Book*	
	Dryer overloaded	See *Use and Care Book*	
	Clothes too damp when put into dryer	See *Use and Care Book*	
	Link blockage	Check Dryer Vent (See p.15 & Procedure #2) See *Use and Care Book*	•
	Dryer loaded with a mixture of fabrics	See *Use and Care Book*	
	Too small a load	See *Use and Care Book*	
	Low voltage at terminal block	CALL SERVICE TECHNICIAN	•••••
	Thermostat(s) inoperative	Check Thermostats (See p.41 & Procedure #13)	•••
7. Clothes do not dry or drying time is too long (gas dryers)	Improper vent installation	Check Dryer Vent (See p.15 & Procedure #2)	•
	Heating system inoperative	Check Gas Assembly (See p.57 & Procedure #17) or (See p.61 & Procedure #18)	••••
	Timer improperly set	See *Use and Care Book*	
	Dryer overloaded	See *Use and Care Book*	
	Clothes too damp when put into dryer	See *Use and Care Book*	
	Link blockage	Check Dryer Vent (See p.15 & Procedure #2) See *Use and Care Book*	•
	Dryer loaded with a mixture of fabrics	See *Use and Care Book*	
	Too small a load	See *Use and Care Book*	
	Low voltage at terminal block	CALL SERVICE TECHNICIAN	•••••
	Thermostat(s) inoperative	Check Thermostats (See p.45 & Procedure #14)	•••

Skill Level Index: • Easy •• Average ••• Difficult •••• Very Difficult ••••• Requires Service Technician

Problem diagnostic charts (continued)

Problem	Possible Cause	Repair Procedure	Skill Level
8. Dryer is noisy	Foreign object in drum front seal	Check Drum (See p.37 & Procedure #12)	•••
	Worn drum bearing	Check Drum Bearing (See p.77 & Procedure #23)	•••
	Dryer not level	Check Leveling (See p.19 & Procedure #4)	•
	Loose panel or component	Check Access & Control Panels (See p.21 & Procedure #5)	••
		Check Wiring and Connections (See p.27 & Procedure #7)	•••
	Foreign object in drum	Check Drum (See p.37 & Procedure #12)	•••
	Worn idler pulley bearing	Check Idler (See p.67 & Procedure #20)	•••
	Worn belt	Check Belt (See p.67 & Procedure #20)	•••
	Damaged or loose blower wheel	Check Blower Wheel (See p.65 & Procedure #19)	•••
	Loose or worn drum slide	Check Drum Slide Assembly (See p.77 & Procedure #23)	•••
9. Dryer runs with door open	Door switch inoperative	Check Door Switch (See p.81 & Procedure #26)	•••
10. Dryer drum does not rotate, but motor runs	Belt off idler pulley	Check Belt (See p.67 & Procedure #20)	•••
	Broken drive belt	Check Belt (See p.67 & Procedure #20)	•••
	Defective idler pulley	Check Idler (See p.67 & Procedure #20)	•••
	Broken idler tension spring	Check Idler (See p.67 & Procedure #20)	•••
	Drum binds	Check Drum Supports (See p.77 & Procedure #23)	•••
11. Damaged dryer body	Scratches and dents	Check Cosmetic Repairs (See p.83 & Procedure #27)	•

Skill Level Index: • Easy •• Average ••• Difficult •••• Very Difficult ••••• Requires Service Technician

Repair procedures

How to use the repair procedures

The following dryer repair procedures take you step-by-step through repairs for most of the dryer problems you are likely to encounter. The Problem Diagnostic Charts on pages 7-11 will help you to pinpoint the likely causes of your problem. Beginning with the most likely cause, you can then refer to the appropriate repair procedure section.

Each repair procedure is a complete inspection and repair process for a single dryer component, containing the information you need to test a component that may be faulty and to replace it, if necessary. This format breaks down even some of the most complex repair problems into separate, easy-to-handle units. Following the instructions given, you can test each component separately, isolating the cause of the problem and replacing any faulty parts. If one procedure fails to locate the failed component, you simply refer back to the Problem Diagnostic Charts for the next most likely cause of the problem.

Featuring a close-up photograph of the component you will be testing, the repair procedure begins with a description of what the component does and how it works. In the case of a component which varies with different dryer models, you will be shown how to determine which type is found on your dryer.

Instructions showing how to test and replace the component begin with steps that must be followed to assure your safety. Other initial steps indicate the skills and equipment that will be needed for the task. If you are uncertain about a process that will be used, such as reading a circuit diagram, using an ohmmeter, or removing access panels, you are referred to the pages in this manual where that process is discussed in detail. No matter what your skill level, careful attention must be paid to these instructions and safety precautions before you begin any procedure.

Clear photographs of typical dryer models illustrate each step of every procedure, proceeding from visual inspection and testing to replacement of the component. Because of the diversity of dryer models available, your dryer may differ somewhat from the illustrated model. However, each procedure has been carefully designed to be representative of the entire GE/Hotpoint lines, and as much information as possible has been included to help you make repairs on most GE/Hotpoint dryers.

NOTE:

The repair procedures are listed below in the order in which they appear in this section. Refer to the Problem Diagnostic Charts on pages 7-11 for the procedure most likely to remedy your problem, then use this list to locate the desired procedure.

Dryer repair procedures

1. Circuit Breakers and Fuses
2. Exhaust Vent
3. Power Cord
4. Leveling Dryer
5. Access and Control Panels
6. Terminal Block
7. Wiring and Connections
8. Selector Switches
9. Start Switch
10. Timer
11. Resistor
12. Drum
13. Electric Dryer Thermostats
14. Gas Dryer Thermostats
15. Moisture Sensor
16. Electric Heater Coils
17. Glo-bar Gas Assembly
18. Spark Ignition Gas Assembly
19. Blower Wheel
20. Belt and Idler
21. Centrifugal Switch
22. Motor
23. Drum Supports
24. Adjusting Dryer Door
25. Door Latch Assembly
26. Door Switch/Dryer Light
27. Cosmetic Repairs

Procedure 1
Inspecting circuit breakers and fuses

Electricity produced by the power company is delivered to your house through a series of connecting power lines. A power distribution panel is located at the point where the main line from the power company enters your home. One of two types of distribution panels services your household – a circuit breaker or a fuse panel. From the distribution panel, the power line is divided into a number of smaller circuits that are distributed to various household appliances, receptacles, and lights. Each of these circuits is protected from becoming overloaded by either a circuit breaker or fuse. It's important to know which breakers or fuses protect each circuit in your home. It's also wise to label them when everything is operating correctly, so that you'll know which breaker or fuse to look for in time of trouble.

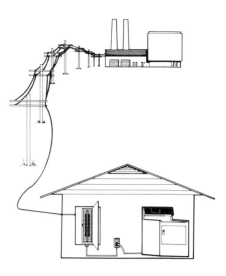

The distribution panel is the place to turn off all power on the dryer circuit before unplugging and servicing it. And it's the first place to look when problems occur. A tripped circuit breaker or blown fuse is a minor problem, but it can stop the entire dryer from working.

Note: There are two 30-amp circuit breakers or fuses controlling the power to your electric dryer; the gas dryer will have only one 15 or 20-amp breaker or fuse. If you are unable to identify the location of the circuit breakers or fuses for your dryer or suspect your dryer is not receiving the correct voltage, contact a qualified electrician.

Circuit breaker type panel   **Fuse type panel**

Circuit breakers and fuses (continued)

Step 1: Be sure all dryer controls are turned **OFF**. Avoid touching any grounded objects such as water pipes when working around power supply. Stand on a dry insulated surface. Other than opening door to distribution panel, never remove any cover or expose any electrical terminals.

Step 2: This procedure requires the use of an ohmmeter. For instructions on how to use an ohmmeter, please refer to Tools and Testing Equipment page 89.

Step 3: <u>Circuit breakers.</u> Circuit breaker distribution panels contain rows of switches. When a breaker "trips", power is shut off, and the breaker switch moves to an intermediate position between the "ON" and "OFF" points.

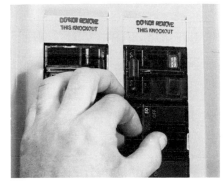

Step 4: To restore power, turn breaker switch to "OFF" position, then back to "ON". If the breaker trips again, the circuit is still overloaded or shorted. Further exploration of the problem is necessary.

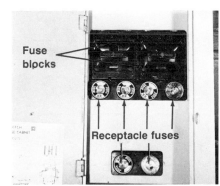

Step 5: <u>Fuses.</u> A second type of distribution panel is protected by fuses. Depending on the age of your home, the fuses controlling your dryer may be small glassfront fuses or cartridge fuses contained in fuse block.

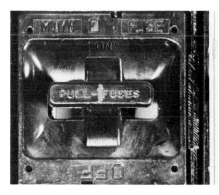

Step 6: Fuse blocks have a separate circuit to which nothing else is attached. A double-pole fuse block (two cartridges joined together at the handle) protect this circuit.

Step 7: Dryer fuses are accessible by pulling block out of panel, which also disconnects dryer. A sharp forward tug releases block.

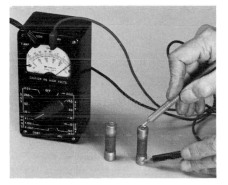

Step 8: Check cartridge fuses with ohmmeter. Touch probes to brass caps on either end of fuse with meter on R X 1 scale. If no continuity, replace fuse.

Step 9: Glassfront fuses unscrew from panel and can sometimes be checked visually for internal breakage. Replace fuse with a known good fuse or check with ohmmeter.

Procedure 2
Inspecting and replacing exhaust vent

Proper venting is essential for the dryer to maintain an unrestricted air flow and the correct air temperature. Exhaust duct installations having either excessive total length or too many turns will reduce air flow and cause problems such as wrinkling of your garments.

If you are having wrinkling problems with your dryer, look at the way the exhaust duct has been installed. Use the charts on this page to give you an idea of what the maximum length for the number of turns and type of hood should be. There are a few high air flow dryers made by GE and Hotpoint that can extend the maximum allowable length. Check the installation instructions that accompany your dryer for further details. Except for these high air flow models, no more than two 90° turns are acceptable. Be sure to count the turn as the ductwork comes out of the dryer and the turn to attach it to the hood.

Four-inch diameter metallic ductwork is recommended. Hoods with both a 4-inch and 2½-inch opening are used, but the 4-inch opening is preferred. The wall cap should be installed with the opening pointed down and spaced at least 12 inches above ground level or any obstruction. The ductwork should be installed so as to prevent back drafts from the outside.

Ductwork that runs through an unheated area or an area adjacent to an air conditioning duct should be insulated to reduce condensation and lint accumulation. Always vent to the outside. Do not vent to a crawl space or other restricted area.

To avoid lint accumulation, do not use screws that extend into the duct to connect the ductwork. Frequently check the bottom of the exhaust vent at the base of the dryer for lint clogging and clean, if necessary.

CAUTION: Do not use nonmetallic flexible ductwork as it can crimp, accumulate lint, and catch on fire.

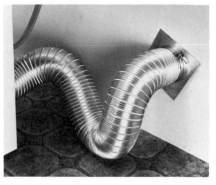

Unacceptable exhaust vent installation

Properly installed exhaust vent

Metallic flexible ductwork specifications

Number of 90° turns separated by at least 4 ft. of straight run	Preferred		2½" OPENING
	Louvered vent	4" OPENING	
0	30 feet		15 feet
1	25 feet (electric) 20 feet (gas)		10 feet
2	10 feet		————

Maximum allowable length of 4" diameter metallic flexible duct.

Rigid ductwork specifications

Number of 90° turns separated by at least 4 ft. of straight run	Preferred 4" OPENING	2½" OPENING
0	45 feet (electric) 35 feet (gas)	30 feet
1	35 feet (electric) 25 feet (gas)	20 feet
2	25 feet (electric) 15 feet (gas)	10 feet

Maximum allowable length of 4" diameter rigid duct.

15

Exhaust vent (continued)

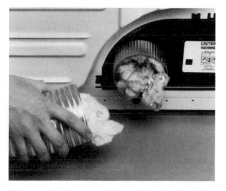

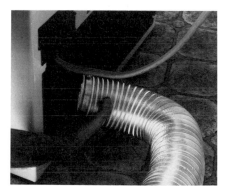

Step 1: For your personal safety, exercise caution when working with any electrical appliance. Watch for sharp edges on vent.

Step 2: Inspection. Periodically, check bottom of ductwork at dryer base for lint accumulation. Remove any lint. Reconnect ductwork.

Step 3: If your ductwork is plastic or appears broken or worn, replace it with metallic 4-inch diameter ductwork.

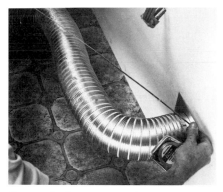

Step 4: Dryer problems also result from improper ductwork installation. If the run is too long or has too many turns, air will not flow right through the dryer. Measure total length of exhaust vent from dryer base to wall cap.

Step 5: Examine the turns in the exhaust ductwork. No turn should be less than 90 degrees, and the more turns, the shorter the run can be. Count the number of turns in the exhaust ductwork from dryer base to wall cap.

Step 6: There should be a minimum of 4 feet between turns. Except for certain high air flow dryers, there should be no more than two 90 degree turns.

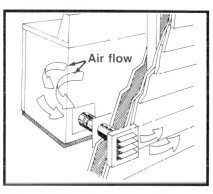

Air flow

Step 7: Measure opening of hood on wall cap. With measurements from Steps 4-7, compare total length of your ductwork with the recommended length on the opposite page. If the configuration of your exhaust vent does not conform, rearrange the position of your ductwork.

Step 8: The flap assembly on the outside vent should also be checked for obstruction and proper operation. Turn on the dryer and check the airflow at this location. Some outdoor vents (see above) have vents that open when the dryer is on and close when it is off. If you have this kind, check to see the vents are opening properly.

Step 9: Replacement or rearrangement. Be sure to follow the specifications listed on the opposite page when replacing or rearranging your ductwork. Failure to do so can cause your dryer to take longer to dry your clothes or possibly overheat and catch fire.

Inspecting and replacing electric dryer power cord

Skill Level Rating: | Easy | Average | **Difficult** | Very Difficult |

The power cord carries power from the electrical receptacle to the dryer's internal wiring. If the dryer fails to operate properly, the power cord could be unplugged or defective. Most problems with the power cord are caused by damaged and loose connections and will likely be visible.

Since the gas dryer power cord is wired directly into the internal wiring with no disconnect access, it can only be inspected visually from the plug to the dryer attachment. Because the gas dryer cord carries less current, fewer problems are encountered with its use. Replacement is a simply a wiring and connection problem (See Procedure 7). **This procedure deals with the testing and replacement of electric power cords.**

The power cord attaches to an electric dryer at the terminal block. Over the years, the terminal block has been located in several areas on the back of the dryer and may be mounted vertically, horizontally, or diagonally. Testing and replacement is the same for all three-wire power cords. Some mobile home dryers have an extra ground wire. For those dryers, follow instructions that come with your part.

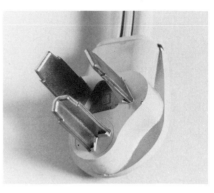

Electric dryer plug

Step 1: Be sure all dryer controls are turned **OFF.** Disconnect power supply at distribution panel. Watch for sharp edges on access panels.

Step 2: This procedure requires the use of an ohmmeter. For instructions on how to use an ohmmeter, please refer to Tools and Testing Equipment, page 89.

Step 3: After protecting floor cover, pull dryer away from wall. Power cord should be visible between dryer and receptacle. Improper connections could be sole cause of trouble.

Step 4: Pull plug from receptacle with a firm, quick tug. Always grasp by plug and never by cord. Be careful not to contact terminal blades of plug. A damaged plug may result from poor connections inside terminal, which can only be checked by qualified electrician.

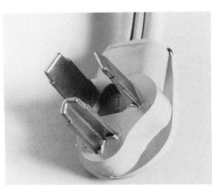

Step 5: Inspect plug carefully for damaged, corroded, or burned terminals. Look carefully around molded portion for signs of overheating. If plug is damaged, replace cord. Do not modify cord in any way or try to convert a 220-volt dryer to 110 volts.

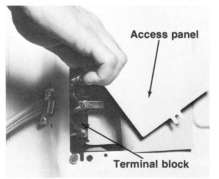

Access panel

Terminal block

Step 6: To inspect power cord at terminal block, remove terminal block access panel by removing mounting screws. If you are not familiar with the location of this panel, refer to Procedure #5: Removing Access and Control Panels.

Electric power cord (continued)

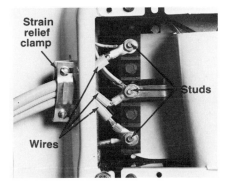

Step 7: Visually inspect power cord connections at terminal block. Inspect wires, studs and strain relief clamp. If any of these parts are damaged, replace defective parts.

Step 8: On some models, the terminal block is horizontal or diagonal rather than vertical. Use the same process to inspect and replace the power cord for whatever configuration.

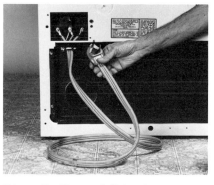

Step 9: If no visible damage to power cord is detected, an ohmmeter must be used to check for defective wires inside the power cord.

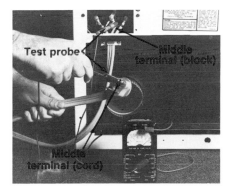

Step 10: To test cord, set ohmmeter on R X 1 scale. Clamp one test probe to terminal block. Middle terminal on block should always indicate continuity to middle terminal on plug.

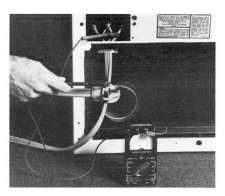

Step 11: Outer terminals on block should indicate continuity to one, but not both, of the outer terminals on plug. With meter probes in place, twist cord to be sure no internal break occurs. Replace cord if needle drops.

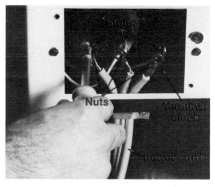

Step 12: To remove power cord, remove ³⁄₈" nuts with nutdriver, holding three eyelets to three studs on terminal block. Remove cord strain relief clamp and pull cord out of dryer.

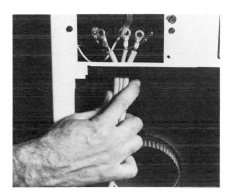

Step 13: Before installing new power cord, brass nuts under terminals must be tight. Assemble cord terminals onto terminal block studs and tighten brass nuts on top of them.

Step 14: CAUTION: To prevent damage to the cord, be sure to reinstall the strain relief clamp. Also be sure to replace access cover to prevent future electrical shock. Reconnect power supply.

Procedure 4
Leveling dryer

Skill Level Rating: | **Easy** | **Average** | **Difficult** | **Very Difficult** |

Your dryer has four leveling feet, one in each corner on the dryer base. Each foot is threaded and screws into the dryer base. Jam nuts are used to lock the feet into position. Ideally, the feet should be adjusted such that the dryer is at the same height as the washer, and sits solidly on the floor. The feet need not be adjusted according to a carpenter's level. If your dryer does not sit solidly on the floor, it may move around.

Leveling feet

Dryer base

Leveling dryer (continued)

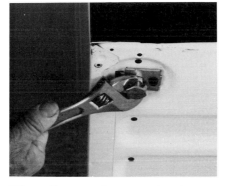

Step 1: Be sure all dryer controls are turned **OFF**. Disconnect power supply at distribution panel and unplug dryer from receptacle. Watch for sharp edges underneath dryer.

Step 2: To adjust leveling foot, loosen jam nut that holds foot to bottom of dryer. Always try to level the dryer by adjusting front feet first.

Step 3: With jam nut loosened, screw foot in or out such that dryer rests solidly on floor. Once foot is in position, tighten jam nut up against dryer base.

Step 4: With your hands on dryer top, try to rock dryer to see if it rests as solidly as possible on floor. If dryer still wobbles, make further adjustments on same foot or other feet.

Procedure 5
Removing access and control panels

Skill Level Rating:	Easy	**Average**	Difficult	Very Difficult

For reasons of safety and appearance, all electrical, gas, and mechanical components of a dryer are enclosed. Many repairs require the removal of access panels to reach affected parts.

The electrical connections are accessed through three main panels--the backsplash control panel, dryer top, and terminal block access. The backsplash control panel houses the controls. Depending on model design, the raised top may expose the high-limit thermostat, electric heater terminals, door switch, and internal wiring. The terminal block access covers the terminal block and power cord connection in electric dryers.

The small access panel centered in the back of the dryer allows the drum to be disengaged from the bearing support. The large, lower access panel in the rear exposes the drive system for inspection. The access panel in the lower right front section on gas dryers permits access to some thermostats and the gas valve and burner assembly.

Most dryer panels are easily removed by taking out the mounting screws securing the panel to the dryer cabinet. However, removal of the dryer backsplash, top, and front panels is more complicated and varies between models. For that reason this procedure refers only to removing the backsplash, top, and front dryer panels. The removal of other panels is described in the procedures requiring their removal.

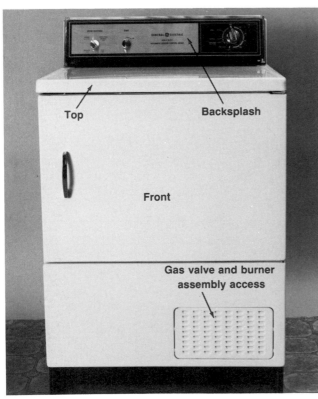

Front panels on gas dryer

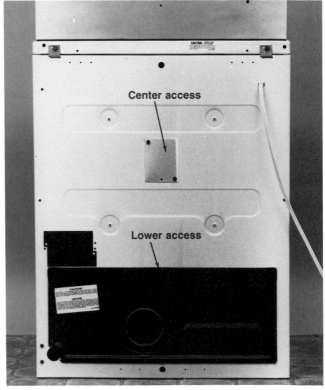

Back panels on gas dryer

21

Access and control panels (continued)

Front panels on electric dryer

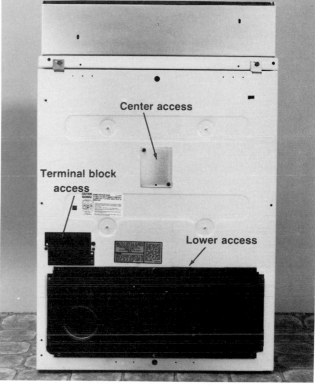

Back panels on standard capacity electric dryer

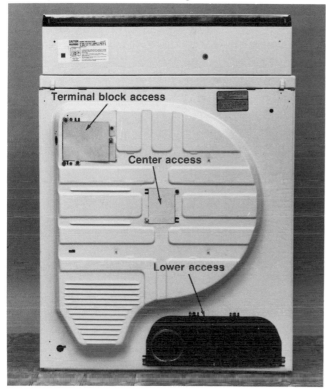

Back panels on some large capacity
electric dryers

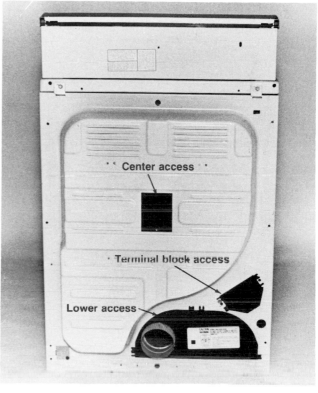

Back panels on other large capacity
electric dryers

Access and control panels (continued)

Step 1: Be sure all dryer controls are turned **OFF**. Disconnect power supply at distribution panel and unplug dryer from receptacle. Watch for sharp edges on access panels.

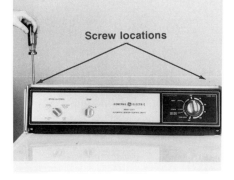

Step 2: The six-inch backsplash. Using a Phillips screwdriver, remove two screws, one at each end of top trim.

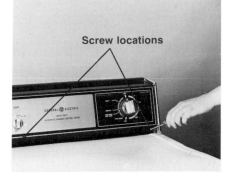

Step 3: Remove two bottom front screws with a Phillips screwdriver.

Step 4: Tilt control panel forward, pulling up gently on wires for full extension. Wires for backsplash controls are now exposed.

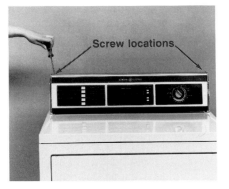

Step 5: The seven-inch backsplash. Using a Phillips screwdriver, remove two top screws on the trim.

Step 6: Lift off top trim and set aside.

Step 7: Remove two Phillips screws from bottom front.

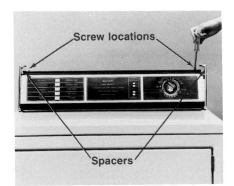

Step 8: Using a nutdriver, remove two hex head screws and spacers from exposed top.

Step 9: Tilt control panel forward, pulling up gently on wires for full extension. Wires for backsplash controls are now exposed.

Access and control panels (continued)

Step 10: Raising cabinet top. On some models, remove four Phillips head screws from upper cabinet front inside door opening. Secure backsplash before tilting back. Note: Rest top firmly against support.

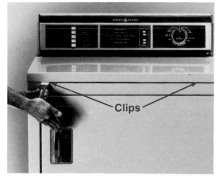

Step 11: Other models have clips that secure top to front panel. To open top, press against clips with a putty knife that has been wrapped with masking tape. Top should pop up. Note: Rest top firmly against support.

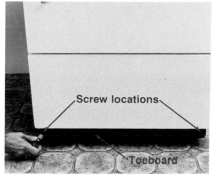

Step 12: Removing cabinet front for any dryer. Loosen, but do not remove, two screws on either side of toeboard with a nutdriver.

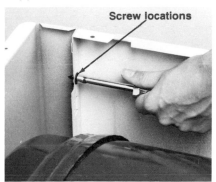

Step 13: Remove two screws on the right and left inside cabinet front with a nutdriver. Remove wire retainers. Lift front up and set to the side, being careful not to damage wiring.

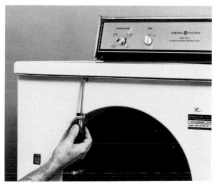

Step 14: When finished with dryer inspection and repair, reassemble dryer and reconnect power supply.

Procedure 6
Inspecting and replacing terminal block

In electric dryers, the power cord is connected to the dryer at the power supply terminal block. From the terminal block, internal wiring carries the power to various circuits of the dryer. Gas dryers do not have a terminal block. Their power cord is connected directly to the internal wiring.

Most problems at the terminal block are caused by loose connections and are visible in the form of either burned and oxidized terminals or damaged insulating material.

Note: The terminal block may be mounted horizontally, vertically, or diagonally, but the inspection and replacement procedure is the same for all types. Some mobile home dryers have a four-wire power cord and terminal block to accommodate an extra ground wire. For those dryers, follow instructions that come with your part.

Terminal block on standard capacity electric dryer

Terminal block on some large capacity electric dryers

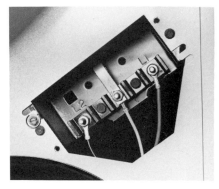

Terminal block on other large capacity electric dryers

Step 1: Be sure all dryer controls are turned **OFF**. Disconnect power supply at distribution panel and unplug dryer from receptacle. Watch for sharp edges on access panels and around terminal block.

Step 2: Remove terminal block access panel by unscrewing mounting screws with nutdriver. This panel is located where power cord attaches to dryer; if you are unfamiliar with this location, refer to Procedure #5: Removing Access and Control Panels.

Step 3: Visually inspect terminal block for burnt terminal connections. If damaged, replace with new terminal block. This vertical mount is common on earlier model large capacity dryers.

Terminal block (continued)

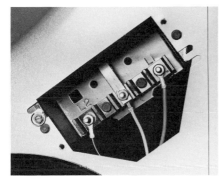

Step 4: On some later large capacity dryers, terminal block is mounted diagonally.

Step 5: On standard capacity dryers, terminal block is mounted horizontally rather than vertically. Use same steps to replace terminal block for any type mounting.

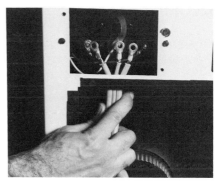

Step 6: To replace terminal block, first remove power cord. Cord is removed by unscrewing three ⅜″ nuts that retain eyelets on terminal block.

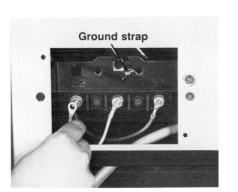

Step 7: Remove 3 inner nuts and remove internal wiring from terminals. When middle wire is removed, ground strap is also released. Move it up and out of your way.

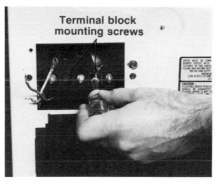

Step 8: Using nutdriver, remove two recessed mounting screws on terminal block. Terminal block can now be lifted out of cabinet.

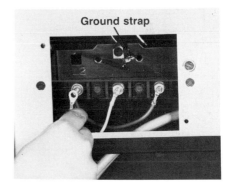

Step 9: Remount new terminal in cabinet. To middle terminal of block, connect white wire of internal wiring and ground strap. CAUTION: Ground strap must be reconnected to prevent damage to your dryer. Attach other wires individually to left and right terminals.

Step 10: Reattach power cord leads to terminal block, making sure that the strain relief clamp is in place and that all wires and nuts are secure.

Step 11: Reassemble dryer and reconnect power supply.

Procedure 7
Repairing wiring and connections

Skill Level Rating: | Easy | Average | **Difficult** | Very Difficult |

Power is carried to the components of the dryer by specially insulated, heat-resistant wire. These wires are connected to various switches and heating systems by push-on terminals, studs, nuts, or connector blocks.

Wires connected to terminals are very susceptible to damage because of arcing and heat build-up. If terminals are dull and oxidized from excessive heat, they should be replaced. Any mating terminal, such as one located on a switch or disconnect terminal, should be polished until bright and shiny before a new wire is attached to assure a good connection.

When checking electrical connections, be sure to follow the circuit diagram for your dryer carefully. The diagram is glued on the back of the dryer or located inside an envelope in the backsplash control panel.

Note: If replacement wire is required, use only appliance wire having the same temperature and gauge rating as the wire you are replacing.

Note: For installation reference make note of how wires are connected. Use masking tape to mark wires or draw a diagram of wiring connections on paper.

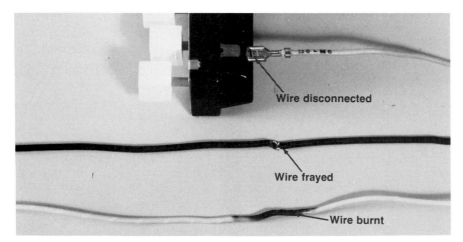

Typical wiring problems encountered

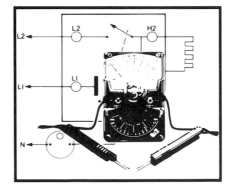

Step 1: Be sure all dryer controls are turned **OFF**. Disconnect power supply at distribution panel and unplug dryer from receptacle. Watch for sharp edges on access panels and parts.

Step 2: This procedure requires use of an ohmmeter and ability to read a circuit diagram. For instructions, please refer to Tools and Testing Equipment, pages 89-92.

Step 3: Most dryer electrical connections are accessed by removing backsplash and raising top. If you are unfamiliar with these processes, please refer to Procedure #5: Removing Access and Control Panels.

Wiring and connections (continued)

Step 4: Some gas dryers have a terminal board located at top left side of dryer. This could be a possible point of wiring and connection problems. To access terminal board, raise dryer top as described in Procedure #5.

Step 5: Either terminal or wire may need repair. Shown above are "push-on" terminals used in dryers. Check wires and terminals visually for signs of damage.

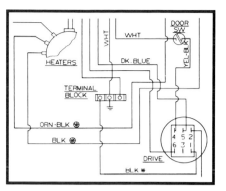

Step 6: Wires are color coded or numbered. Follow wire on your circuit diagram to find where it is connected.

Step 7: To test a particular wire, disconnect one end from male terminal connection and place ohmmeter probes across both ends of wire. You should observe continuity on R x 1 scale.

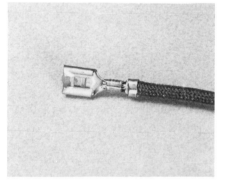

Step 8: If no continuity, check area where wire is attached to female terminal. Wires should make contact against terminal. If attachment looks okay, replace wire.

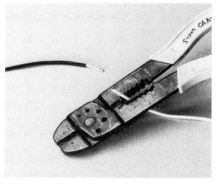

Step 9: To remove insulation from the wire use wire strippers rather than knife to avoid cutting too deep. Remove only enough insulation to make connection or splice.

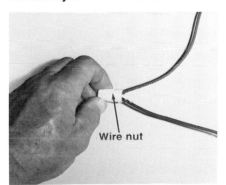

Step 10: To splice dryer wiring use only high temperature wire nut. Strip the insulation back to bright and shiny wire. Twist strands together and secure with wire nut.

Step 11: Should terminal need replacing, cut old terminal loose from wire. Strip wire end and twist strands together. Slip new terminal over twisted wire strands and crimp terminal down over them securely with a terminal crimping tool.

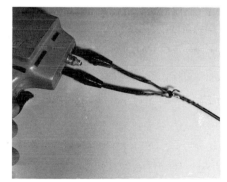

Step 12: If you do not have a crimping tool, you will have to solder terminals on. Twist wire strands together. Place terminal over them and solder. Reassemble dryer and reconnect power supply when finished.

Procedure 8
Inspecting and replacing selector switches

Skill Level Rating: | Easy | Average | Difficult | **Very Difficult**

Selector switches, located on the backsplash control panel, allow you to select the correct drying cycle for the type of clothes you are drying. Typical selections include NORMAL, FLUFF, DELICATES, PERMANENT PRESS, and COTTONS. Once selected, the switch then activates the heating control system to supply NORMAL HEAT, LOW HEAT, or NO HEAT to dry your clothes. There are three types of selector switches used – toggle, rotary, and pushbutton.

If the dryer does not heat, or the air temperature is wrong for a particular cycle, there could be a malfunction in the selector switches. If the dryer won't start, there may be a problem in the start switch located on or near the selector switch panel. See Procedure #9: Inspecting and Replacing Start Switch.

Internal wiring

Rotary selector switch

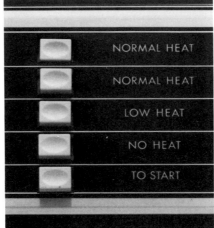

Pushbutton selector switch

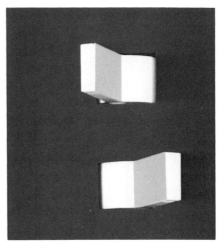

Toggle selector switch

Step 1: Be sure all dryer controls are turned **OFF.** Disconnect power supply at distribution panel and unplug dryer from receptacle. Watch for sharp edges on and inside backsplash.

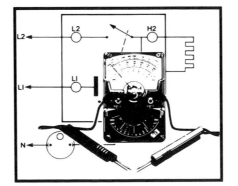

Step 2: This procedure requires use of an ohmmeter and ability to read a circuit diagram. For instructions, please refer to Tools and Testing Equipment, pages 89-92.

Step 3: Remove backsplash control panel. If you are unfamiliar with this process, please refer to Procedure #5: Removing Access and Control Panels.

Selector switches (continued)

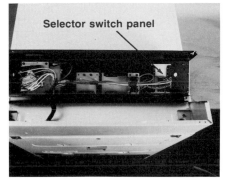

Step 4: Wiring to selector switch panel is located directly behind controls on inside of backsplash.

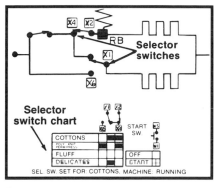

Step 5: Look carefully at your circuit diagram located inside backsplash or on back of your dryer. Find numbers for selector switch terminals (X) used in affected drying cycle from the selector switch chart.

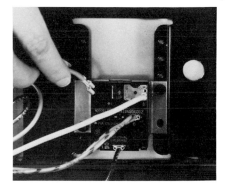

Step 6: When you have located the terminals for the switch contacts controlling the affected cycle, remove the wire leads from these terminals.

Step 7: Turn selector switch to affected cycle. Place ohmmeter probes across two switch terminals. If no continuity on R x 1 scale, replace switch.

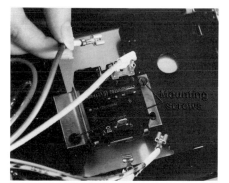

Step 8: Remove other wire leads to switch panel. For installation reference, make note of how wires are connected. Remove selector switch panel from its support by removing 2 mounting screws with nutdriver.

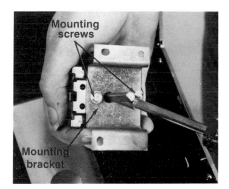

Step 9: Rotary switch knobs may have to be pulled off shaft from front of backsplash for switch removal. Some switches are also attached to a mounting bracket which is removed by removing 2 mounting screws with nutdriver.

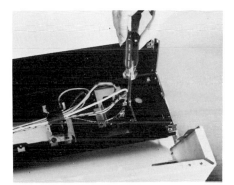

Step 10: Install new selector switch, making sure all connections are secure and in right location.

Step 11: Reassemble dryer and reconnect power supply.

Procedure 9
Inspecting and replacing start switch

Skill Level Rating: | Easy | Average | Difficult | **Very Difficult**

The start switch on the backsplash activates the drive motor through a set of contacts on the centrifugal switch. On pushbutton control dryers, the start switch is at the bottom of the selector switch panel; rotary start switches are to the right of the selector switch.

If the contacts in the start switch are defective, the dryer will not run. The start switch is primarily a safety feature. It prevents the dryer from running when the door is open and must be reactivated each time the drying cycle is stopped by opening the door.

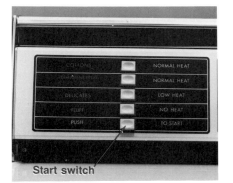

Pushbutton start switch

Rotary start switch

Step 1: Be sure all dryer controls are turned **OFF**. Disconnect power supply at distribution panel and unplug dryer from receptacle. Watch for sharp edges on and inside backsplash.

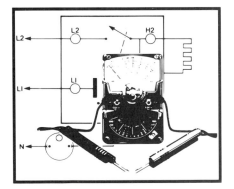

Step 2: This procedure requires use of an ohmmeter and ability to read a circuit diagram. For instructions, please refer to Tools and Testing Equipment, pages 89-92.

Step 3: Remove backsplash control panel. If you are unfamiliar with this process, please refer to Procedure #5: Removing Access and Control Panels.

Start switch (continued)

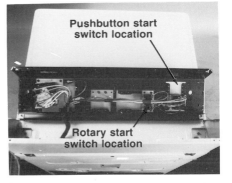

Step 4: Wiring to start switch is located directly behind controls on inside of backsplash.

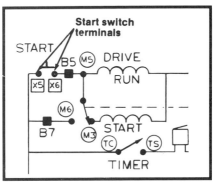

Step 5: Look carefully at your circuit diagram, located inside backsplash or on back of your dryer. Find letter and numbers used for start switch terminals for your dryer.

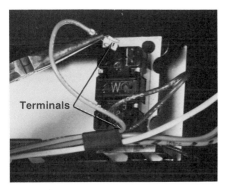

Step 6: When you have located contact terminals for start switch, remove wire leads from switch terminals. Shown above is rotary switch.

Step 7: Place ohmmeter probes across two switch terminals. Depress or turn switch to "ON". If no continuity on R x 1 scale, replace switch.

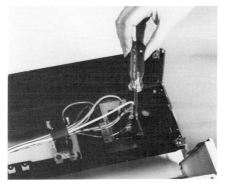

Step 8: If start switch is on selector switch panel, remove and replace as described in Procedure #8: Inspecting and Replacing Selector Switches, Steps 8-10.

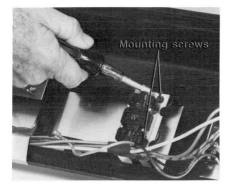

Step 9: To remove rotary start switch, remove two mounting screws with nutdriver. Remove other wire leads to switch. Pull knob off its shaft from front of backsplash.

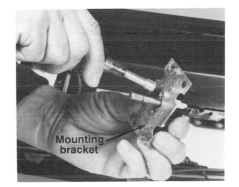

Step 10: The rotary switch is attached to a mounting bracket which is removed by removing two mounting screws underneath switch with nutdriver.

Step 11: Install new start switch, making sure all wire connections are secure. Attach switch to mounting bracket and secure switch on backsplash support. Attach knob to shaft.

Step 12: Reassemble dryer and reconnect power supply.

Inspecting and replacing timer

Skill Level Rating:	Easy	Average	Difficult	**Very Difficult**

The timer is located inside the backsplash control panel directly behind the cycle control knob. The motor within the timer advances the timer in the drying cycle selected. After a specified period of time, the timer switches open to turn off the heat and stop the drum from turning.

For different cycles, the timer functions differently. In the timed cycle the timer runs continuously for the amount of time set on the dial. In the automatic cycle the timer advances when the thermostats turn the heat off and will continue to advance until the heat comes back on. The total cycle time depends on the type of fabrics, size load, moisture content, and timer setting. On electronic moisture sensing models, the timer advances when the clothes reach the specified level of dryness.

Many dryer problems can result from bad electrical connections within the timer. The dryer may not run, heat, or complete its cycle. Should the timer knob advance in the timed cycle but not during the automatic cycle, check the resistor as outlined in Procedure #11: Inspecting and Replacing Resistor, or the moisture sensor as described in Procedure #15: Inspecting and Replacing Moisture Sensor.

Timer control knob

Timer motor and wiring

Step 1: Be sure all dryer controls are turned **OFF**. Disconnect power supply at distribution panel and unplug dryer from receptacle. Watch for sharp edges inside backsplash.

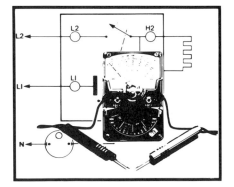

Step 2: This procedure requires use of an ohmmeter and ability to read a circuit diagram. For instructions, please refer to Tools and Testing Equipment, pages 89-92.

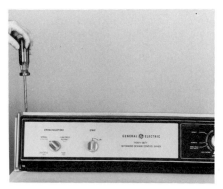

Step 3: Remove backsplash control panel. If you are unfamiliar with this process, please refer to Procedure #5: Removing Access and Control Panels.

Timer (continued)

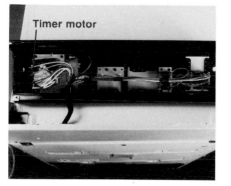

Step 4: Wiring to timer is located directly behind cycle control knob on inside of backsplash.

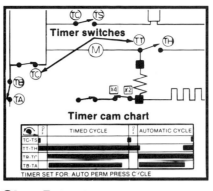

Step 5: Look carefully at your circuit diagram, located inside backsplash or on back of your dryer. Find letters used for timer switch terminals (T) that control dryer circuit of concern. Timer cam chart shows which switches are open and closed for each cycle.

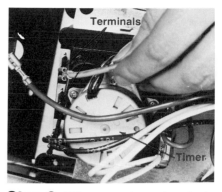

Step 6: When you have located terminals for switch controlling affected cycle, remove wire leads from these terminals. For installation reference make note of how wires are connected.

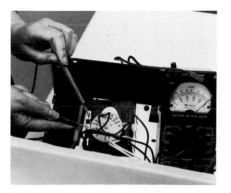

Step 7: Turn timer control knob to cycle where those timer contacts should be closed. Place ohmmeter probes across the 2 switch terminals. If no continuity with ohmmeter set on R × 1 scale, replace timer.

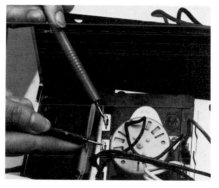

Step 8: Find timer motor winding terminals from circuit diagram and remove wire leads from them. Set ohmmeter on R × 100 scale and place probes on these leads. Meter should sweep upscale. If not, replace timer.

Step 9: Remove timer from its support by removing two mounting screws with nutdriver. Remove wire leads to timer. For installation reference, make note of how wires are connected.

Step 10: Pull off the timer rotary knob on backsplash to remove timer. Timer is attached to a mounting bracket which is removed by removing 2 mounting screws with nutdriver.

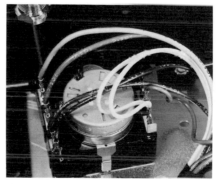

Step 11: Install new timer, reattaching wires as stated in instructions that come with timer. Make sure all connections are properly placed and secure.

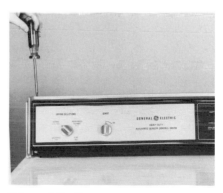

Step 12: Reassemble dryer and reconnect power supply.

Inspecting and replacing resistor

Skill Level Rating: | Easy | Average | **Difficult** | Very Difficult |

The resistor is only used in electric dryers having an automatic cycle. It is located either between the selector switches and the timer on the inside of the backsplash or under the top of the dryer near a board of electrical connections. During the automatic cycle, the timer is not energized until the heaters are turned off. Because the timer runs on 110 volts and not the 220 volts that pass through the heaters, the resistor divides the heater voltage in half to provide the correct voltage to the timer.

Should the resistor malfunction, the timer won't advance in the automatic cycle. If the timer is good, it should advance in the timed cycle. If the timer does not advance in either cycle, check the timer as described in Procedure #9: Inspecting and Replacing Timer.

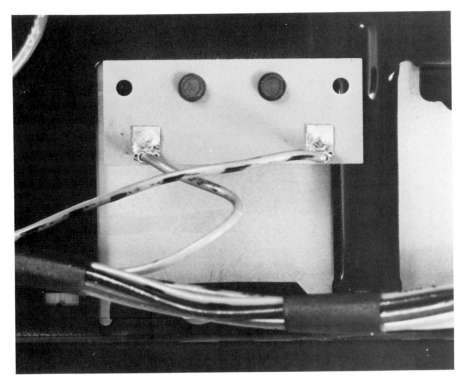

Close-up of resistor terminal board

Resistor (continued)

Step 1: Be sure all dryer controls are turned **OFF.** Disconnect power supply at distribution panel and unplug dryer from receptacle. Watch for sharp edges on access panels.

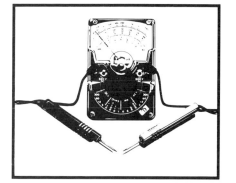

Step 2: This procedure requires the use of an ohmmeter. For instructions on how to use an ohmmeter, please refer to Tools and Testing Equipment, page 89.

Step 3: Remove backsplash control panel. If you are unfamiliar with this process, please refer to Procedure #5: Removing Access and Control Panels.

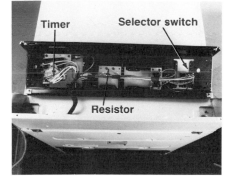

Step 4: The resistor is located between the selector switch and timer when it is located inside the backsplash. It is rectangular in shape.

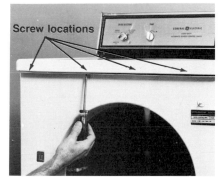

Step 5: If the resistor is not inside the backsplash, raise the dryer top and look for it near a board of electrical connections to the side of the drum. If you are unfamiliar with this process, Please refer to Procedure #5: Removing Access and Control Panels.

Step 6: Remove one wire lead from resistor terminal board.

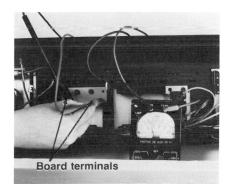

Step 7: Attach ohmmeter probes to two board terminals. Set on R X 100 scale, ohmmeter should read about 38 ohms. If not, replace resistor.

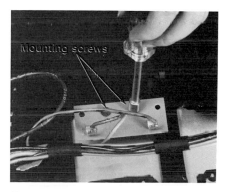

Step 8: Remove resistor terminal board from mounting bracket by removing mounting screws with nutdriver.

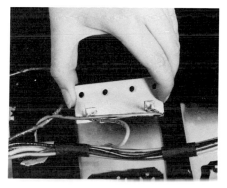

Step 9: Be sure you are replacing with a resistor of the correct resistance and wattage. Replace wire leads and make sure all connections are tight. Reassemble dryer and reconnect power supply.

Procedure 12
Removing drum

Skill Level Rating: | Easy | Average | **Difficult** | Very Difficult |

The drum is by far the largest dryer component and takes up the majority of space inside the dryer. To access some dryer components, the drum must be removed.

The drum is connected to the motor shaft by a belt that is held taut over a torsion bar or a spring-loaded idler pulley system. The drum is also connected to the rear of the dryer cabinet by a drum shaft and a retaining ring.

Dryer noise may result from foreign objects (usually pocket contents) in the drum or drum seal. Steps 2-4 of this procedure pertain to drum noise.

CAUTION: The belt is under high tension on the torsion bar or spring-loaded idler. Be careful when you swing back the bar or the idler arm to release the belt that it does not snap back and pin your hand.

Drum removal (front view)

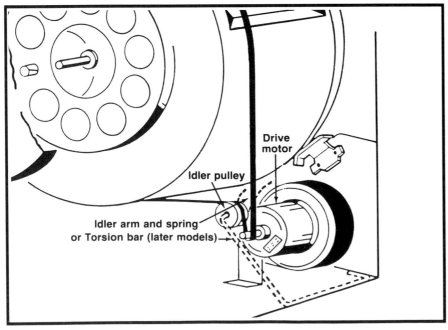

Dryer drive system (rear view)

Removing drum (continued)

Step 1: Be sure all dryer controls are turned **OFF**. Disconnect power supply at distribution panel and unplug dryer from receptacle. Watch for sharp edges on access panels and parts.

Step 2: Drum noise. Should dryer make excessive noise, revolve inside of drum to check for foreign objects such as hair pins or contents from clothes pockets.

Step 3: If you hear noise when revolving drum, but nothing is in drum, look for foreign object in front drum seal. To access seal, remove dryer front. If you are unfamiliar with this process, refer to Procedure #5: Removing Access and Control Panels.

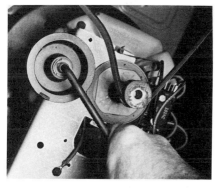

Step 4: Turn front panel of dryer around to inspect felt front seal. Visually inspect felt for sharp or pointed objects before moving your hands around it. Remove any foreign objects.

Step 5: Drum removal. Remove large, lower rear access panel by unscrewing all 5/16″ mounting screws around cabinet with nutdriver. Detach belt from idler pulley as described in Procedure #20.

Step 6: For more recent dryers, release belt by pulling torsion bar down, as shown. Belt should pop off.

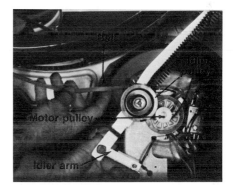

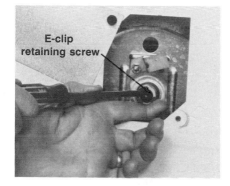

Step 7: For earlier model standard capacity dryers, swing idler arm away from pulleys as shown, and belt should pop off easily.

Step 8: For earlier model large capacity dryers, pull back idler arm away from pulleys as shown, and belt should pop off.

Step 9: To release drum, first remove center rear access panel by removing the two 5/16″ mounting screws with nutdriver. Then use small screwdriver to pry retaining ring loose.

Removing drum (continued)

Step 10: Raise and support dryer top. If you are unfamiliar with this process, please refer to Procedure #5: Removing Access and Control Panels.

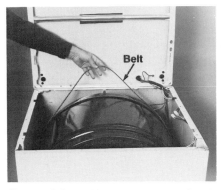

Step 11: When you have raised top, move loose belt back behind the drum out of your way.

Step 12: Remove dryer front. If you are unfamiliar with this process, refer to Procedure #5: Removing Access and Control Panels.

Step 13: Before you can lift out the dryer drum on some large capacity dryers (B and earlier), you must remove the two drum slides. Use a nutdriver to remove the mounting screws.

Step 14: Lift up drum to remove slide, being careful not to knock slide into dryer.

Step 15: Carefully lift drum out through dryer front. Avoid hitting the sides of dryer with drum.

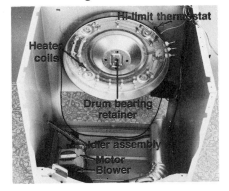

Step 16: With drum removed, you can access the drum bearing, heater coils, motor, idler, blower, and some thermostats.

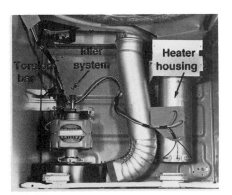

Step 17: On some models, the heater coils are on the floor of the dryer, and the idler system has a torsion bar instead of a spring-loaded idler.

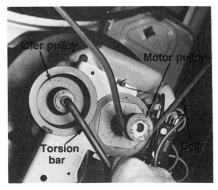

Step 18: When reassembling dryer, reinstall drum and position belt around drum and rethread belt over top of idler pulley and underneath motor pulley with torsion bar pulled away from pulleys.

Removing drum (continued)

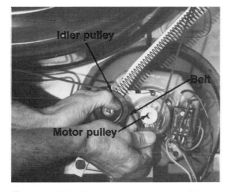

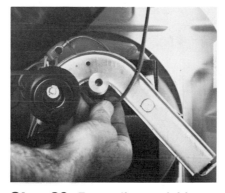

Step 19: If you have an earlier model standard capacity dryer as shown above, position belt over old marks on drum and rethread belt over top of idler pulley and underneath motor pulley with idler arm pulled away from pulleys.

Step 20: For earlier model large capacity dryers, rethread belt over top of idler pulley and underneath motor pulley with idler arm pulled away from pulleys, as shown.

Step 21: Check belt alignment by turning drum in both directions. Complete dryer reassembly and reconnect power supply.

Procedure 13
Inspecting and replacing electric dryer thermostats

Skill Level Rating:	Easy	Average	**Difficult**	Very Difficult

Thermostats cycle the electric heaters on and off, based on their sensing of the air temperature. Electric dryers generally have two or more thermostats – the drum outlet thermostat(s) and the hi-limit thermostat. The drum outlet thermostat(s) senses the temperature of the air flowing out of the drum and turns off the heaters at the correct air temperature. The hi-limit thermostat acts as a safety if the drum outlet thermostat malfunctions or the air flow becomes restricted. It is located on the heater housing, either behind the drum or on the dryer base.

In standard capacity dryers, the drum outlet thermostat is located inside the lint trap. Some models have two drum outlet thermostats, one for the normal drying cycle, and another for the delicate cycle. On large capacity dryers the drum outlet thermostat will be located either to the left of the lint trap or on the internal exhaust duct.

To locate the thermostats on your electric dryer, check your dryer's circuit diagram. Circuit diagrams are located in an envelope inside the backsplash or are taped on the back of your dryer. If you are unfamiliar with how to open the backsplash control panel, please refer to Procedure #5: Removing Access and Control Panels. On some earlier models, thermostat locations are not shown on the circuit diagram; use the illustrations on the next page to help you locate the thermostat locations for your dryer.

Note: The test described in the following procedure shows only whether the thermostat is open or closed. The test can only verify a switch malfunction, the most common problem with thermostats. It cannot, however, determine if the thermostat is cycling at the proper temperature. Temperature calibration can only be checked by a qualified service technician. If the test in this procedure shows no defect in the thermostat switch, check dryer venting and door alignment for air leaks before calling for service.

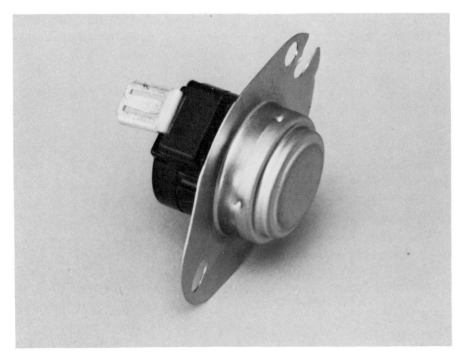

Dryer thermostat

Electric dryer thermostats (continued)

Thermostat locations for large capacity electric dryers

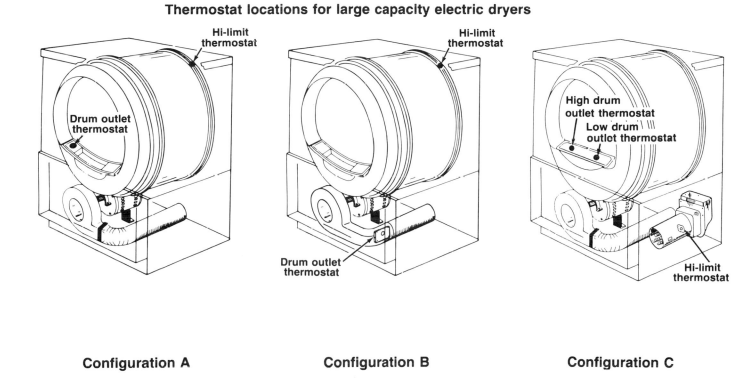

Configuration A   **Configuration B**   **Configuration C**

Thermostat locations for standard capacity electric dryers

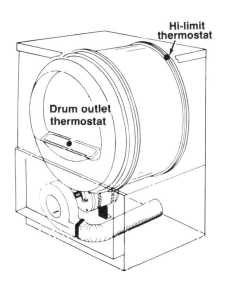

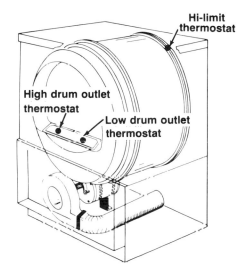

Configuration A   **Configuration B**

Electric dryer thermostats (continued)

Step 1: Be sure all dryer controls are turned **OFF**. Disconnect power supply at distribution panel and unplug dryer from the receptacle. Watch for sharp edges on access panels and parts.

Step 2: This procedure requires the use of an ohmmeter. For instructions on how to use an ohmmeter, please refer to Tools and Testing Equipment, page 89.

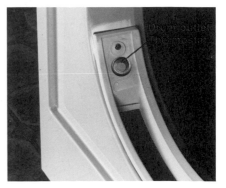

Step 3: Open dryer door and look near lint trap. There may be one or two thermostats visible in front or to left of lint trap.

Step 4: Remove the thermostat mounting screws. On some models, thermostats are mounted with Torx® screws. Access thermostat wire leads.

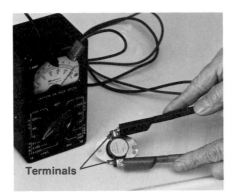

Step 5: Remove one wire leading to thermostat and place ohmmeter probes across thermostat terminals. With ohmmeter set on R x 1 scale, test for continuity. If no continuity, replace thermostat.

Step 6: To replace, remove thermostat by removing mounting screws or nuts with a nutdriver or Torx driver. Install new thermostat.

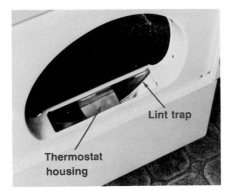

Step 7: On some models, you will have to remove lint trap to access thermostat(s). Underneath lint trap, there is a metal housing that protects thermostat(s) from lint.

Step 8: Remove the two screws on the back side of thermostat housing. On some models, this housing is mounted with Torx screws. Lift out housing. Thermostats are tested and replaced as described in Steps 5 and 6.

Step 9: Hi-limit thermostat is located on heater housing. On some models, this housing is in back of the drum and is accessed by raising dryer top. If you are unfamiliar with this process, please refer to Procedure #5: Removing Access and Control Panels.

Electric dryer thermostats (continued)

Step 10: The hi-limit thermostat on these models is located on top right side of heater housing. This thermostat is tested and replaced as described in Steps 5 and 6.

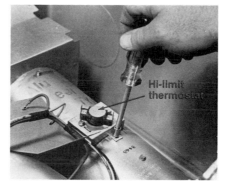

Step 11: On other models, the hi-limit thermostat is located on top of a heater housing in the bottom of the dryer. This thermostat is tested and replaced as described in Steps 5 and 6.

Step 12: To access the drum outlet thermostat on some large capacity dryers, remove dryer front. If you are unfamiliar with this process, please refer to Procedure #5: Removing Access and Control Panels.

Step 13: When the front is removed, you can easily access the drum outlet thermostat on the internal exhaust duct. It can be tested and replaced as described in Steps 5 and 6.

Step 14: When you have finished testing and replacing thermostats, reassemble dryer and reconnect power supply.

Procedure 14
Inspecting and replacing gas dryer thermostats

Skill Level Rating:	Easy	Average	**Difficult**	Very Difficult

Thermostats cycle the gas burner on and off based on their sensing of the air temperature. Standard capacity gas dryers have three or four thermostats, and large capacity dryers have four. All gas dryers have a drum outlet thermostat for normal on-off cycling of the gas valve control, and an inlet hi-limit thermostat that turns off the gas valve should the dryer overheat or the air flow become restricted. Some gas dryers use a drum inlet thermostat in combination with a drum outlet thermostat to regulate low heat; others have a delicate thermostat for low heat control. Large capacity dryers may also have a blower housing thermostat as an additional safety.

Over the years in dryer design, there have been two arrangements of thermostat locations used for standard capacity gas dryers and three arrangements of thermostat locations used for large capacity gas dryers. Your dryer will have one of the arrangements illustrated on the next page. For later dryer models, thermostat locations are pictured on your dryer's circuit diagram.

Note: The test described in the following procedure shows only whether the thermostat is open or closed. The test can only verify a switch malfunction, which is the most common problem with thermostats. It cannot, however, determine if the thermostat is cycling at the proper temperature. Temperature calibration can only be checked by a qualified service technician. If the test in this procedure shows no defect in the thermostat switch, check dryer venting and door alignment for air leaks before calling for service.

CAUTION: Do not use open flame around gas assembly.

Dryer thermostat

45

Gas dryer thermostats (continued)

Thermostat locations for large capacity gas dryers

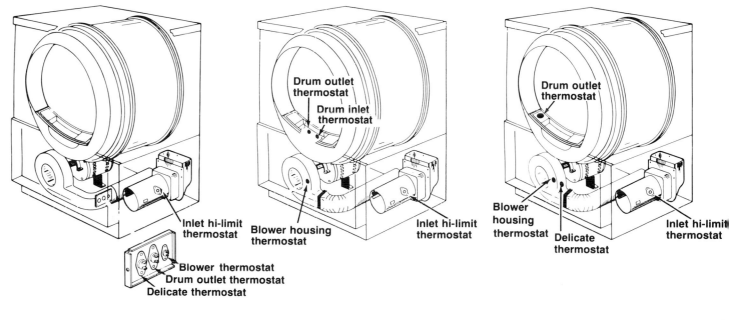

Configuration A

Configuration B

Configuration C

Thermostat locations for standard capacity gas dryers

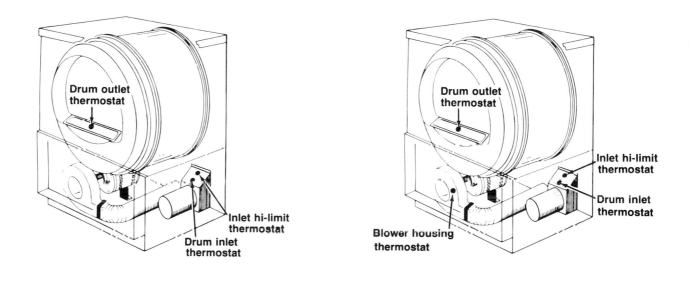

Configuration A

Configuration B

Gas dryer thermostats (continued)

Step 1: Be sure all dryer controls are turned **OFF**. Disconnect power supply at distribution panel and unplug dryer from receptacle. Watch for sharp edges on access panels and parts. Do not use open flame around gas assembly.

Step 2: This procedure requires the use of an ohmmeter. For instructions on how to use an ohmmeter, please refer to Tools and Testing Equipment, page 89.

Step 3: Open dryer door and look near lint trap. There may be one or two thermostats visible in front or to left of lint trap.

Step 4: Remove the thermostat mounting screws. On some models, thermostats are mounted with Torx® screws. Access thermostat wire leads.

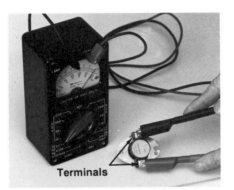

Step 5: Remove one wire leading to thermostat and place ohmmeter probes across thermostat terminals. With ohmmeter set on R x 1 scale, test for continuity. If no continuity, replace thermostat.

Step 6: To replace, remove thermostat by removing mounting screws or nuts with a nutdriver or Torx driver. Install new thermostat.

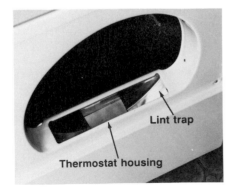

Step 7: On some models, you will have to remove lint trap to access thermostat(s). Underneath lint trap, there is a metal housing that protects thermostat(s) from lint.

Step 8: Remove the two screws on the back side of thermostat housing. On some models, this housing is mounted with Torx screws. Lift out housing. Thermostats are tested and replaced as described in Steps 5 and 6.

Step 9: To access other thermostats, remove drum from dryer. If you are unfamiliar with this process, please refer to Procedure #12: Removing Drum.

Gas dryer thermostats (continued)

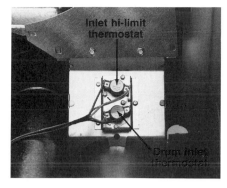

Step 10: With drum removed, you can easily access rear duct thermostats. These thermostats are tested and replaced as described in Steps 5 and 6.

Step 11: Depending on dryer model, there may also be a thermostat on the back side of the blower housing. This thermostat is tested and replaced as described in Steps 5 and 6.

Step 12: The combustion chamber is located just beyond gas valve assembly. The thermostat mounted on top right side is tested and replaced as described in Steps 5 and 6.

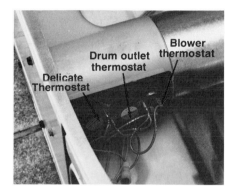

Step 13: On internal exhaust duct you can access drum outlet, delicate, and blower thermostats on some models. These thermostats are tested and replaced as described in Steps 5 and 6.

Step 14: Reassemble dryer and reconnect power supply.

Procedure 15
Inspecting and replacing moisture sensor

Skill Level Rating: | Easy | Average | **Difficult** | Very Difficult |

The moisture sensor is used in certain dryer models having an automatic cycle. The sensor is a copper-plated grid that can be mounted two different ways behind the lint trap. One way (Type A) is visually apparent when you open the door; the other (Type B) is on the other side and cannot be seen without looking inside the drum. Moisture coming in contact with the sensor completes an electrical circuit to a printed circuit board in the backsplash. When this circuit is completed to the printed circuit board, the timer will not advance. When the clothes reach a predetermined dryness, the circuit from the sensor opens, and the timer motor is energized.

The sensor could either short out, in which case the timer will not advance to turn off the dryer, or it could be open, in which case, the timer will advance too soon and turn the dryer off with wet clothes.

Note: If the dryer does not advance in the automatic cycle, check to see if it will advance in the timed cycle. If the timer advances in the timed cycle, check the moisture sensor. If the timer does not advance in either cycle, check the timer as described in Procedure #10: Inspecting and Replacing Timer.

Printed circuit board

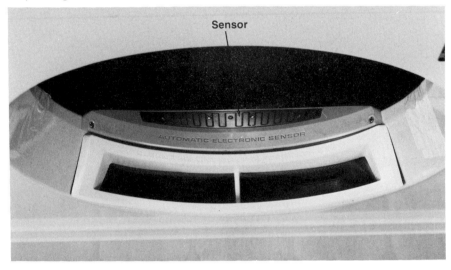

Type A sensor location (looking into dryer with door open)

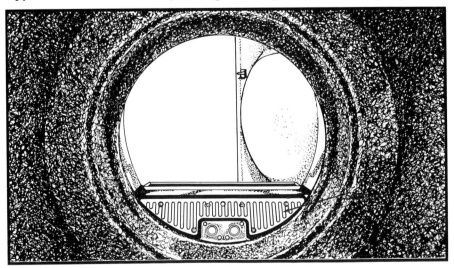

Type B sensor location (as seen from inside the dryer looking out)

49

Moisture sensor (continued)

Step 1: Be sure all dryer controls are turned **OFF**. Disconnect power supply at distribution panel and unplug dryer from receptacle. Watch for sharp edges inside dryer door and backsplash.

Step 2: This procedure requires the use of an ohmmeter. For instructions on how to use an ohmmeter, please refer to Tools and Testing Equipment, page 89.

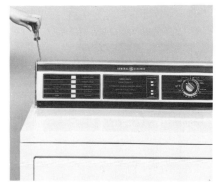

Step 3: Remove backsplash control panel. If you are unfamiliar with this process, please refer to Procedure #5: Removing Access and Control Panels.

Step 4: The printed circuit board for moisture sensor is located between selector switch panel and timer inside the backsplash.

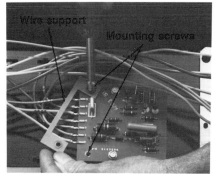

Step 5: Some printed circuit boards have a wire support to secure wire leads. Remove wire support by removing 2 mounting screws with a nutdriver.

Step 6: To test wire leads C and G, remove leads from terminals marked C and G on circuit board.

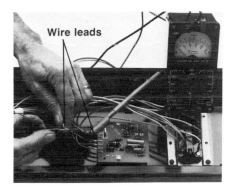

Step 7: Attach ohmmeter probes to wire leads from C and G terminals. Set ohmmeter on highest scale. If needle moves partially upscale, go to Step 9. If not, go to Step 8.

Step 8: With ohmmeter still connected to wire leads from C and G terminals, set ohmmeter to R × 100 scale. Rub a moist sponge across the sensor. If no continuity, replace moisture sensor. (See Step 12).

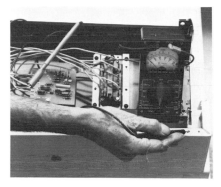

Step 9: Place ohmmeter probes consecutively across C and G wire leads and dryer cabinet. Set ohmmeter on highest scale. If needle moves partially upscale, go to Step 10. If not, see Step 12 to replace sensor.

Moisture sensor (continued)

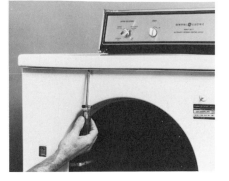

Step 10: To see if wires need straightening or replacing, raise dryer top. It may also help to remove dryer front. If you are unfamiliar with these processes, refer to Procedure #5: Removing Access and Control Panels.

Step 11: Find wires leading to sensor and test as described in Procedure #7: Repairing Wiring and Connections. Cut and splice to repair wire or replace wire with same type as removed.

Step 12: To remove sensor on dryer frame behind lint trap, remove two Phillips head mounting screws connecting sensor housing to dryer cabinet. Sensor housing can then be pulled forward through dryer door for easy access.

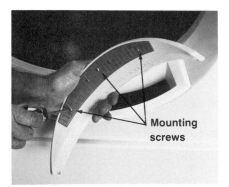

Step 13: By removing three sensor mounting screws with a Phillips screwdriver, remove sensor from housing to inspect wire leads or to replace.

Step 14: To remove sensor inside drum, first remove lint filter and locate metal housing that protects the thermostats from lint.

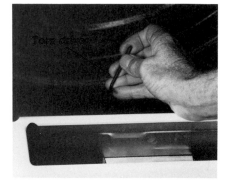

Step 15: Remove two screws on back of housing. On some models, housing is mounted with Torx® screws. Lift out housing.

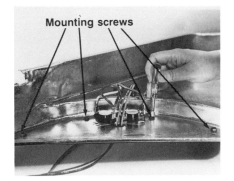

Step 16: Remove four 5/16″ hex-head screws inside trap duct. (To show screw locations for picture, sensor was removed from dryer). Lift sensor housing gently and inspect wire leads. Straighten leads, if necessary.

Step 17: Harness wires must be cut and spliced to remove and replace sensor. Sensor and housing are replaced as a complete assembly.

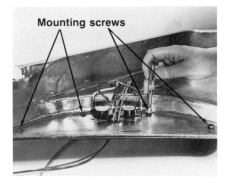

Step 18: Reattach sensor housing to lint trap, then install metal housing back over thermostats. Replace lint filter.

Moisture sensor (continued)

Step 19: If moisture sensor checks out good, and timer advances in the timed but not automatic cycle, replace circuit board by removing two mounting screws with nutdriver.

Step 20: Remove wire leads from printed circuit board. For installation reference, make note of how wires are connected. Labeling wires is recommended.

Step 21: To install new circuit board, attach wire leads to their correct location and mount board with two screws. Be sure to reattach wire support. Make sure all connections are secure. Reassemble dryer and reconnect power supply.

Procedure 16
Inspecting and replacing electric heater coils

Skill Level Rating:	Easy	Average	Difficult	**Very Difficult**

Heat is supplied in electric dryers by two identical resistance coils. The coils, located behind the drum in earlier models and under the drum in later models, are mounted in parallel inside a heater housing and receive power from two legs for a 240-volt line. The heaters are controlled in some models by one or more selector switches, offering the option of high heat (both heaters on), low heat (one heater on), or fluff (both heaters off). Thermostats cycle the heaters on and off. Air is pulled across the heaters before entering the drum. An unrestricted air flow is crucial to optimum heater performance.

When evaluating a dryer heating problem, first determine whether or not the dryer is getting any heat. If you are getting low heat, but not high heat, one coil may be defective, or there may be a problem in one of the selector switch contacts. By determining that your dryer is getting some heat, you have eliminated problems in the timer, thermostats, motor centrifugal switch, and power supply.

If the dryer runs, but there is no heat, first check the circuit breakers or fuses. One breaker or fuse may be tripped. Using your circuit diagram and an ohmmeter, you can then check the heaters, selector switches, thermostats, timer and motor centrifugal switch as outlined in problem 2 on page 8.

If one heater is defective, it is wise to replace both heaters at the same time. Also look for signs of overheating from restricted air flow. Check the lint filter and dryer vent for clogging and improper installation.

Heater coils behind drum (front view with drum removed)

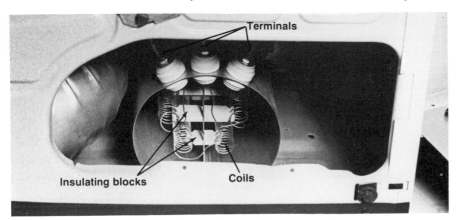

Heater coils under drum (front view with front panel removed)

53

Electric heater coils (continued)

Step 1: Be sure all dryer controls are turned **OFF**. Disconnect power supply at distribution panel and unplug dryer from receptacle. Watch for sharp edges on access panels and parts.

Step 2: This procedure requires the use of an ohmmeter. For instructions on how to use an ohmmeter, refer to Tools and Testing Equipment page 89.

Step 3: In many electric dryers, heater coils are mounted behind the drum. To access terminals for testing, raise dryer top. If you are unfamiliar with this process, refer to Procedure #5: Removing Access and Control Panels.

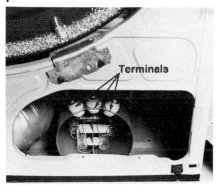

Step 4: On some newer models, heater coils are located underneath the drum on the right front side. To access terminals for testing, remove dryer front. If you are unfamiliar with this process, refer to Procedure #5: Removing Access and Control Panels. Locate terminals and proceed to Step 16.

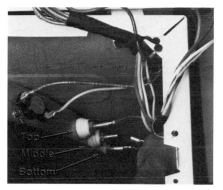

Step 5: To test heater coils located behind the drum, remove wire leads from top terminal and one of the other terminals. Middle terminal is connected to inner coil. Bottom terminal is connected to outer coil.

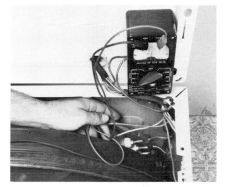

Step 6: Place ohmmeter probes across top terminal and one other terminal. If no upscale movement on R x 1 scale, replace coil. Keeping probe on top terminal, repeat test for other terminal.

Step 7: If either heater is defective, remove drum. If you are unfamiliar with this process, refer to Procedure #12: Removing Drum.

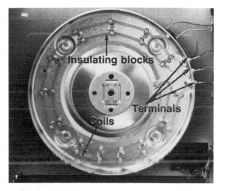

Step 8: When the drum is removed, you can visually check heater coils for breaks.

Step 9: To replace defective coil in housing behind drum, cut both ends of coil at the terminals. Remove the two terminals by unscrewing nuts on either side of the housing.

Electric heater coils (continued)

Step 10: Wrap one end of a new coil around top of a new terminal between two washers tightened on each side by a nut.

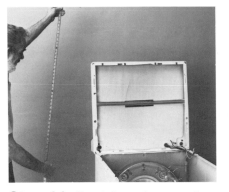

Step 11: Stretch replacement coil to the proper length – 49½″ for outer coil and 42½″ for inner coil. CAUTION: For proper performance, each coil must be stretched evenly and maintain its desired length when released.

Step 12: Remove defective heater coil(s) from heater assembly and thread replacement coil through the insulators. Be sure coils are evenly spaced. Check insulators for cracks or breaks, replacing any that are defective.

Step 13: Wrap other end of coil around top of the second terminal between two washers. Using two wrenches, tighten two nuts which hold coil in place.

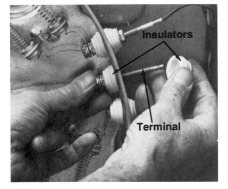

Step 14: Insert terminals through one insulator, then through the correct hole in the heater housing, then through another insulator. Secure on the outside of housing with a nut.

Step 15: When replacing both coils, two identical replacement kits are needed. Repeat Steps 9-14 to replace second coil. It is recommended when replacing one coil to replace the other at the same time.

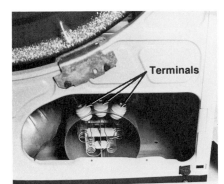

Step 16: To test terminals for coils located underneath the drum, remove terminal leads and place ohmmeter probes across left terminal and one other terminal.

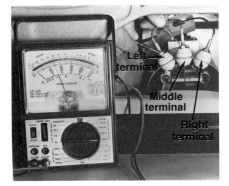

Step 17: Set ohmmeter on R x 1 scale and look for resistance reading of about 20 ohms. Keeping probe on left terminal, repeat test for other terminal. If either test fails, replace heater assembly.

Step 18: To replace heater assembly, remove drum. If you are unfamiliar with this process, refer to Procedure #12: Removing Drum.

Electric heater coils (continued)

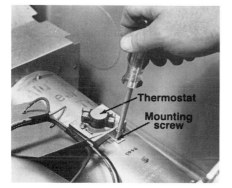

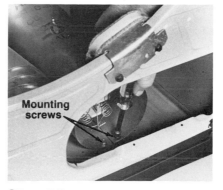

Step 19: Detach wire leads to thermostat on top of heater assembly, noting how wires reconnect. Remove thermostat bracket from top of assembly by unscrewing one mounting screw with nutdriver. Set thermostat aside for reattachment to new heater assembly.

Step 20: Using a 5/16" nutdriver, remove two mounting screws that hold assembly to base of dryer.

Step 21: Carefully lift heater assembly up and out of dryer. CAUTION: Assembly is sharp around edges and fits very tightly into back hole. Insert new heater assembly and reattach mounting screws, thermostat bracket, and terminal leads.

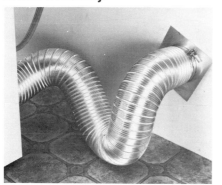

Step 22: After installing new heater(s), look for signs of restricted air flow (improperly installed vent shown above, lint blockage, etc.) that could have caused coils to overheat and burn out. Check vent and lint filter as described in Procedure #2: Inspecting and Replacing Exhaust Vent.

Step 23: Reassemble dryer and reconnect power supply.

Procedure 17
Inspecting and replacing glo-bar gas assembly

Skill Level Rating: | Easy | Average | Difficult | **Very Difficult** |

The gas burner assembly regulates and ignites the gas that will heat the dryer air. The gas must pass through two valves that are opened electromagnetically by the solenoid gas valves. The gas then passes over an electric igniter "glow bar" that ignites it. When the flame detector senses a flame, it turns the igniter off. Dryer thermostats cycle the flame on and off according to air temperature. If the dryer runs but does not heat, there could be problems with thermostats, centrifugal switch, timer switches, or selector switches, instead of the gas assembly. See the Diagnostic Chart on page 8.

Three components of the gas assembly can be checked — the valve coils, the igniter, and the flame detector. On most models, the igniter is located underneath the burner assembly at the rear; the flame detector is mounted on the combustion chamber. There is a newer gas assembly that has the valve coils located one behind the other and slightly different disconnects. It is tested and repaired the same way.

If your gas dryer is an older model and makes a clicking noise when turned on, it likely has a spark ignition gas assembly. See Procedure # 18 for inspection and repair of this type of heating system.

CAUTION: This procedure should only be attempted by an experienced do-it-yourselfer. If after making the checks suggested in this procedure, your gas assembly still does not work, call a qualified service technician for service.

CAUTION: Be sure the gas to the dryer is turned OFF before disassembling the gas assembly. Use a flashlight to illuminate work area. Never smoke or use an open flame or match around gas assembly. See Step 24 for testing gas leaks.

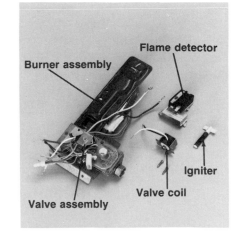

Gas assembly components

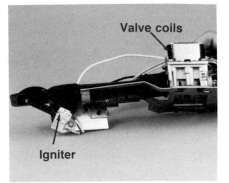

Side view new gas assembly

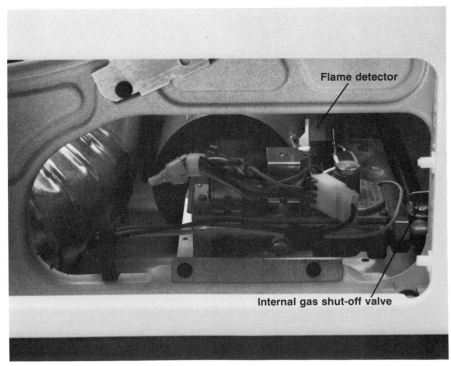

Gas assembly location (front panel removed)

Glo-bar gas assembly (continued)

Step 1: Never smoke or use an open flame or match when working around gas assembly. When examining gas assembly in Steps 4 and 5, keep hands outside of dryer.

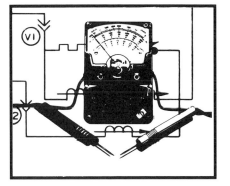

Step 2: This procedure requires use of an ohmmeter and ability to read a circuit diagram. For instructions, please refer to Tools and Testing Equipment, pages 89-92.

Step 3: Open gas assembly access panel at bottom right side of dryer front. Place your hand underneath bottom of dryer and push panel outward. Watch for sharp edges on access panel.

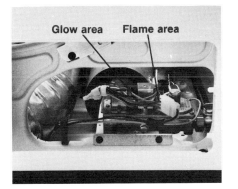

Step 4: With dryer on and drum turning, look for a glow and a flame from inside gas assembly. If you see a glow and flame for 30 seconds or longer, all components of gas assembly are functioning normally. Check no further.

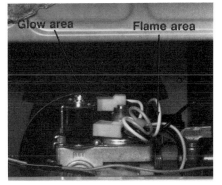

Step 5: If you have a newer gas assembly, it will look slightly different. The glow and flame areas are noted above. If you see a glow and flame for 30 seconds or longer, all components of the gas assembly are functioning okay.

Step 6: To examine a defective gas assembly, turn shut-off valve in your household gas supply line **OFF.** Turn all dryer controls **OFF.** Disconnect power supply at distribution panel and unplug dryer from receptacle. Watch for sharp edges on parts.

Step 7: Turn internal gas shut-off valve to "OFF" position by turning handle counterclockwise.

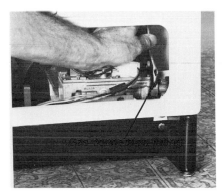

Step 8: To remove valve and burner assembly for inspection, loosen gas connection fitting with an adjustable wrench by pushing wrench to rear of dryer. Lay connection pipe to the side.

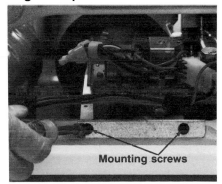

Step 9: Using a 5/16-inch nutdriver, remove two mounting screw connecting valve assembly to cabinet front.

Glo-bar gas assembly (continued)

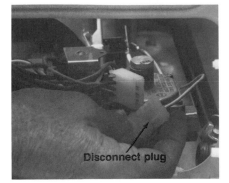

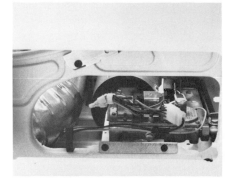

Step 10: Disconnect any plugs connecting wiring to gas assembly.

Step 11: If flame detector is located on combustion chamber, remove wire leads from it to free gas assembly. If detector is attached to side of gas assembly, carefully pull assembly outside dryer for inspection. The igniter on the bottom rear is very fragile.

Step 12: If in Step 4 or 5 there was no glow, igniter or flame detector is defective (see Steps 13-16). If there was glow but no flame, valve coils are defective (see Steps 17-21). If flame came on but went out immediately, check detector (Steps 13-14) and valve coils (Steps 17-21).

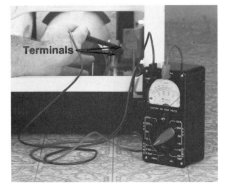

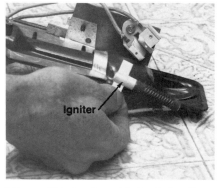

Step 13: Flame detector. With wire leads removed from flame detector, place ohmmeter probes across exposed terminals. If meter shows no continuity on R X 1 scale, replace flame detector.

Step 14: To remove flame detector, remove one screw from front side with nutdriver and lift detector up and out. Mounting bracket comes with detector. Remount new detector and reconnect assembly.

Step 15: Igniter. Detach igniter from a spring-loaded clip underneath burner assembly and inspect carefully. Igniter is very brittle and fragile. Replace if burned or oxidized.

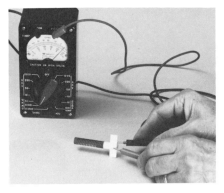

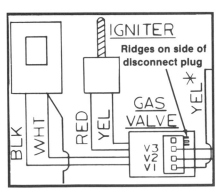

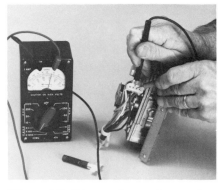

Step 16: To test igniter, set ohmmeter on R X 100 scale and place probes across sides at silver-coated end of igniter. Replace if needle does not move partially upscale.

Step 17: Valve coils. Using circuit diagram that comes with your dryer locate V1, V2, and V3 on the disconnect plug on front of valve assembly.

Step 18: Place ohmmeter probes across V2 and V3 on disconnect plug. Replace valve coil if needle does not move partially upscale on R X 100 scale. Test terminals V1 and V3 to check other valve coil.

59

Glo-bar gas assembly (continued)

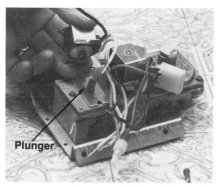

Step 19: Remove mounting screw holding wire strain relief clip. For installation reference, make note of how wires are connected to valave coil. Remove wire leads attached to bell connector or disconnect plug from valve coil.

Step 20: The valve coil replacement kit will have two new coils. It is recommended that you replace both coils even if only one is defective. To remove valve coil, remove two mounting screws on valve coil bracket with screwdriver or nutdriver.

Step 21: CAUTION: To avoid gas leaks, be sure "O" ring gasket fits securely in groove around plunger. Place new valve coil over plunger and reattach mounting screws and wire leads. You will need a new bell connector to replace any you removed.

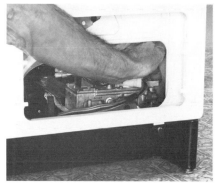

Step 22: Reinsert valve assembly into access. Place wire leads onto flame detector, reattach disconnect plugs, and screw mounting screws back into cabinet. Reattach gas connection fitting by screwing nut toward you with adjustable wrench.

Step 23: Open internal gas shut off valve by turning handle clockwise. Turn on gas in household supply line.

Step 24: Check for gas leaks by applying a 50:50 mixture of water and dishwashing liquid to pipe fitting joints. If bubbles form, shut off gas and recheck connections. Do not operate dryer or leave gas supply turned on until leak is corrected. Close access panel and reconnect power supply.

Procedure 18

Inspecting and replacing spark ignition gas assembly

Skill Level Rating: | Easy | Average | Difficult | **Very Difficult** |

While the Glo-Bar gas igniter (see Procedure #17: Inspecting and Replacing Glo-Bar Gas Assembly) is the most common way gas is ignited on GE/Hotpoint dryers, two other ignition methods were used on earlier models. One, the standing pilot method, has a small flame that is lit much like a gas furnace and burns constantly. The standing pilot gas assembly is recognizable by the red-tipped pilot reset lever at the front of the assembly. This gas assembly should only be repaired by a qualified service technician and is not covered in this manual.

The other method, called spark ignition, ignites the gas electrically when needed by arcing current acorss two igniter blades and generating a "spark". When the flame detector senses the presence of the gas flame, it shuts off the igniter and energizes the main valve coil to start the flow of gas heat to the dryer. The solenoid-operated valve coils are held energized by a warp resistor relay. If for some reason there is no flame or no gas, the warp resistor switch will heat up and de-energize the gas valves. The circuit will remain off or "locked" out until power is removed for about 5 minutes, allowing cool down and reset.

Note: If the dryer runs but does not heat, there could be problems with thermostats, centrifugal switch, timer switches, or selector switches, as well as with the gas assembly. See the Problem Diagnostic Chart on page 8.

CAUTION: This procedure should only be attempted by an experienced do-it-yourselfer. If after making the checks suggested in this procedure, your gas assembly still does not work, call a qualified service technician for service.

CAUTION: Be sure the gas to the dryer is turned OFF before disassembling the gas assembly. Use a flashlight to illuminate work area. Never smoke or use an open flame or match around gas assembly. See Step 26 for testing gas leaks.

Spark ignition gas assembly

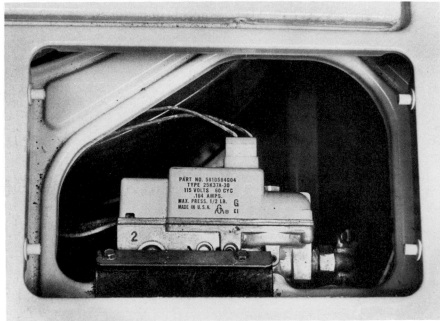

Gas assembly location (front panel removed)

61

Spark ignition gas assembly (continued)

Step 1: Never smoke or use an open flame or match when working around gas assembly. When examining gas assembly in Step 4, keep hands outside of dryer.

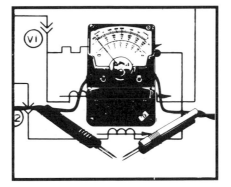

Step 2: This procedure requires use of an ohmmeter and ability to read a circuit diagram. For instructions, please refer to Tools and Testing Equipment, pages 89-92.

Step 3: Open gas assembly access panel at bottom right side of dryer front. Place your hand underneath bottom of dryer and push panel outward. Watch for sharp edges on access panel.

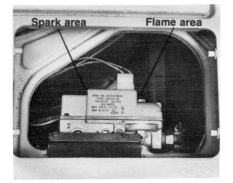

Step 4: With dryer on and drum turning, look for a spark and a bluish flame from inside gas assembly. If you see a flame for 30 seconds or longer, all components of gas assembly are functioning normally. Check no further. If flame is yellow, call a qualified service technician for adjustment.

Step 5: To examine a defective gas assembly, turn shut-off valve in your household gas supply line **OFF**. Turn all dryer controls **OFF**. Disconnect power supply at distribution panel and unplug dryer from receptacle. Watch for sharp edges on parts.

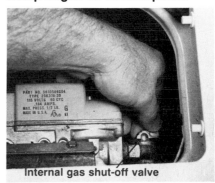

Step 6: Turn internal gas shut-off valve to "OFF" position by turning handle counter-clockwise.

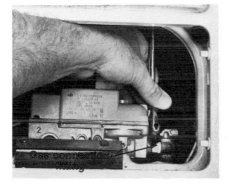

Step 7: To remove valve and burner assembly for inspection, loosen gas connection fitting with an adjustable wrench by pushing wrench to rear of dryer. Lay connection pipe to side.

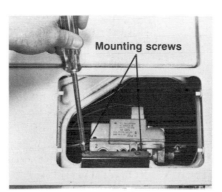

Step 8: Using a 5/16" nutdriver, remove two mounting screws connecting valve assembly to cabinet front.

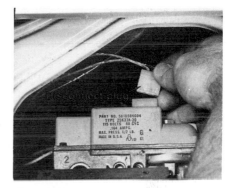

Step 9: Pull out disconnect plug from front of valve assembly to disconnect wiring.

Spark ignition gas assembly (continued)

Step 10: Pull assembly outside of dryer for access and remove mounting screw that attaches cover to assembly. Lift off cover to test individual components.

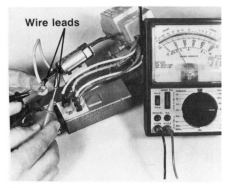

Step 11: Igniter. Inspect igniter tips. They should not appear worn and should make good contact. Using your circuit diagram, place ohmmeter probes on detached wire leads going to flame detector terminals S and s. If no continuity on R X 1 scale or if igniter tips are worn, replace igniter.

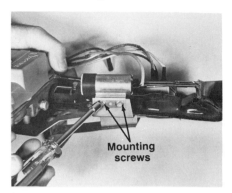

Step 12: To remove old igniter, detach the two mounting screws that hold igniter to mounting bracket. Your new igniter will look different from the old igniter. Some mounting modification is necessary.

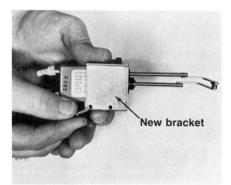

Step 13: Following the instructions that come with your new part, select the mounting bracket that goes with your burner assembly and attach igniter to it using mounting screws.

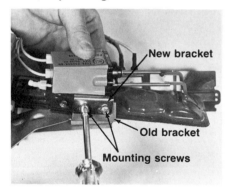

Step 14: Reattach new mounting bracket over old bracket and refasten two mounting screws to secure igniter to assembly. Position igniter as shown in part instructions so blade does not touch burner tube and short out.

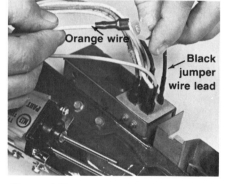

Step 15: Attach yellow wire from igniter to small S terminal on flame detector. Connect male end of new black jumper wire to orange igniter wire and female end of black jumper to large S terminal on flame detector.

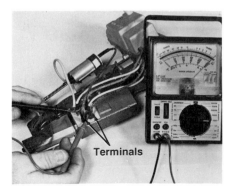

Step 16: Flame detector. To test flame detector, place ohmmeter on the smaller S terminal and B terminal. With ohmmeter set on R X 1, check for continuity. If no continuity, replace flame detector.

Step 17: To replace, remove two mounting screws that hold it to the burner assembly. Depending on your model, replacement part may require some mounting modification. Follow instructions that come with the new part.

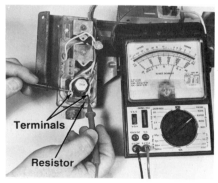

Step 18: Resistor. Test resistor when gas assembly has been off for at least 5 minutes. Place ohmmeter probes across two resistor terminals. With ohmmeter set on R X 100, check for some resistance. If none, replace resistor.

Spark ignition gas assembly (continued)

Step 19: To remove resistor, unscrew the two mounting screws that attach the wire terminals to resistor. Lift old resistor off and install new resistor.

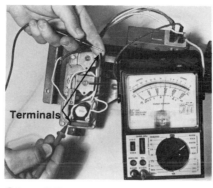

Step 20: <u>Valve coils.</u> Isolate wire leads going to each valve coil. One lead will be black going to coil, and the other white going from coil to resistor. Remove bell connector to access wires.

Step 21: Place ohmmeter probes on wires for each coil and check for resistance reading on R X 100 scale. If none, replace valve coil(s).

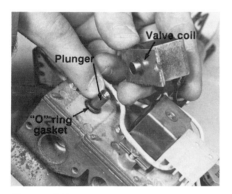

Step 22: To remove old valve coil, remove two mounting screws that attach cover to bracket.

Step 23: CAUTION: To prevent gas leaks, make sure "O" ring gasket is securely placed in groove around plunger. Place coil over plunger and reattach wire leads. Attach new bell connector for any you removed.

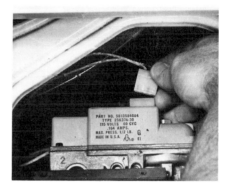

Step 24: When repairs are completed, reattach cover to gas assembly. Reinsert gas assembly back into access, secure mounting screws, and reconnect disconnect plug.

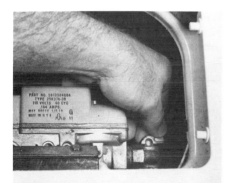

Step 25: Reattach gas connection fitting and open internal shut-off valve by turning handle clockwise. Turn on gas in household supply line.

Step 26: Apply a 50:50 mixture of water and dishwashing liquid to pipe fitting joints. If bubbles form, shut off gas and recheck connections. Do not operate dryer or leave gas supply turned on until leak is corrected.

Step 27: Replace access cover and reconnect power supply.

Inspecting and replacing blower wheel

Skill Level Rating: | Easy | Average | **Difficult** | Very Difficult |

The blower is an exhaust fan that circulates air through the dryer. It pulls moist air out of the drum and directs it out through the exhaust ductwork. The suction the blower creates pulls incoming air across the heating source before the air can enter the drum. Proper air flow is important for the dryer to maintain the right temperature for the drying cycle.

The blower wheel, located inside the bottom left front of the dryer cabinet, is clamped onto the motor shaft. Should the clamp loosen or the wheel blades wear or break, the wheel could be off-balance, and the dryer will make noise. If the blower wheel cannot turn freely, the clothes will take a long time to dry. The blower wheel is also susceptible to lint accumulation.

Blower location

Step 1: Be sure all dryer controls are turned **OFF**. Disconnect power supply at distribution panel and unplug dryer from receptacle. Watch for sharp edges on access panels and parts.

Step 2: To inspect blower wheel, remove dryer front. If you are unfamiliar with this process, please refer to Procedure #5: Removing Access and Control Panels.

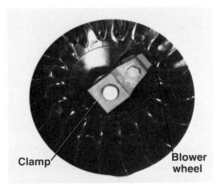

Step 3: Check blower wheel through cabinet opening. Look for broken blades and see if blower wheel turns freely; it should not rub blower housing in any way. Remove blockages or lint.

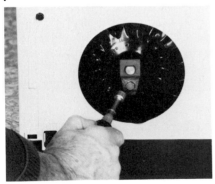

Step 4: If blower is rubbing on housing, loosen (but do not remove!) clamp screw with nutdriver and reposition wheel on shaft where it does not rub. Retighten screw on clamp.

Step 5: To replace blower wheel, remove drum. If you are unfamiliar with this process, please refer to Procedure #12: Removing Drum.

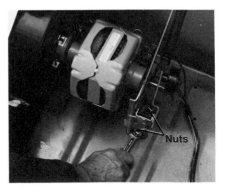

Step 6: To access blower wheel, motor assembly must be moved toward rear of dryer base. Remove two nuts on base of rear motor support with adjustable wrench.

Blower wheel (continued)

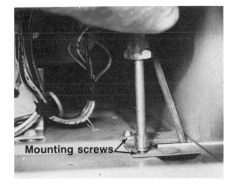

Step 7: On models with a torsion bar idler system, you will have to release bar by removing two mounting screws that hold bar to dryer base.

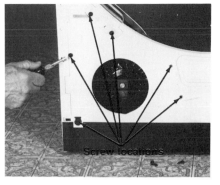

Step 8: Remove 6 mounting screws from front cabinet around blower housing using nutdriver.

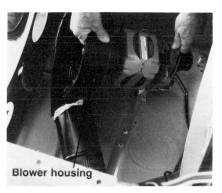

Step 9: Once blower housing is removed from front of cabinet and unscrewed from internal ductwork, blower, motor, and idler can be lifted and moved for easier access.

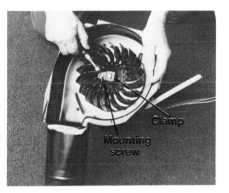

Step 10: The blower wheel is removed by unscrewing mounting screw on clamp with nutdriver. The clamp has two pieces that go in front and in back of blower wheel.

Step 11: Remove front green piece of clamp and lift blower wheel off shaft. Save the clamp.

Step 12: Place back side of clamp (black) on shaft. Position front side of clamp (green) on top of new blower and place on shaft so that back side of clamp is threaded through blower. Reattach screw to clamp, but do not tighten firmly.

Step 13: Carefully align blower, motor, and idler assembly into its original position. Attach rear motor support back to dryer base. Reattach torsion bar, if any, to dryer base.

Step 14: Replace cabinet screws around blower housing.

Step 15: After making certain through cabinet opening that blower is aligned properly and wheel turns freely, tighten clamp screw down. Reassemble dryer and reconnect power supply.

Procedure 20
Inspecting and replacing belt and idler

Skill Level Rating: | Easy | Average | **Difficult** | Very Difficult

The belt drives the drum through a pulley system attached to the motor shaft. The belt is held securely in place over an idler pulley and under a motor pulley by a spring-loaded arm or torsion bar that is part of the idler assembly. The idler assembly is attached to the rear motor support at the bottom left rear of the dryer. The configuration and parts of the idler assembly vary in different model dryers, as shown below.

Note: The only times you need to check the belt and idler is if the motor runs but the drum does not rotate, or if the dryer is noisy and the noise has been traced to the idler. Causes for the drum not to rotate include broken belt, belt off the idler, loose motor pulley, or broken idler spring. Noise can be caused by the belt off of the idler, a broken belt, or worn idler bearings.

CAUTION: Be careful when bending back idler arm or torsion bar; each is under high tension and could snap back on your hand.

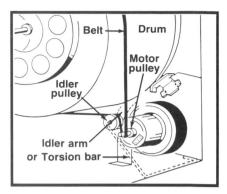

Dryer drive system

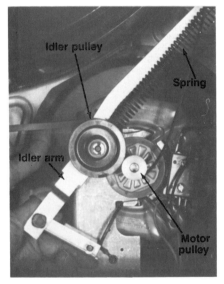

Type A – Earlier model standard capacity idler assembly

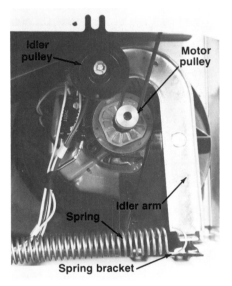

Type B – Earlier model large capacity idler assembly

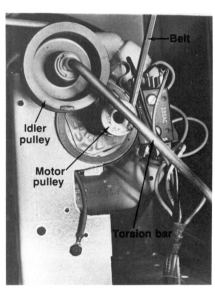

Type C – New idler assembly design

Step 1: Be sure all dryer controls are turned **OFF**. Disconnect power supply at distribution panel and unplug dryer from receptacle. Watch for sharp edges on access panels and parts.

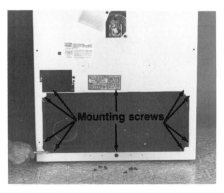

Step 2: Remove large, lower rear access panel by unscrewing 5/16" mounting screws with nutdriver.

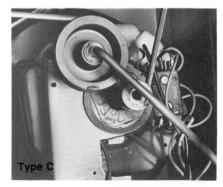

Step 3: Determine which type of idler system is present in your dryer using the photos above. Steps 4-15 refer to the Type A system; Steps 16-22 to Type B; and Steps 23-29 to Type C.

Belt and idler (continued)

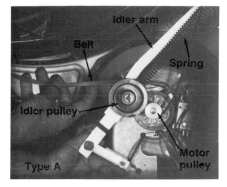

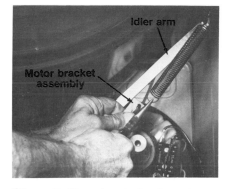

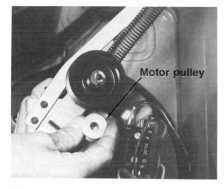

Step 4: Inspecting Type A. Examine each component of the idler assembly for visible damage. Check belt to see if it is worn, broken, or off of idler. If belt is off of idler, check spring for any breaks.

Step 5: If spring is broken, leave belt off of idler pulley and unhook spring. Hook one end of new spring onto idler arm and other end into hole on arm of motor bracket assembly.

Step 6: If belt is securely in place and drum does not rotate, check to see if pulley on motor shaft will turn freely. If the motor shaft does not turn, check both motor and blower as described in Procedures #19 and #21.

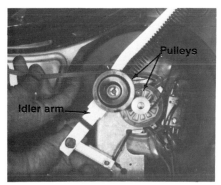

Step 7: If belt needs replacing, make sure it is first off of idler pulley. Swing idler arm away from pulleys, and belt should pop off. CAUTION: Be careful that arm does not snap back on your hand.

Step 8: To replace belt, dryer top must be raised and dryer front removed. If you are unfamiliar with these processes, refer to Procedure #5: Removing Access and Control Panels.

Step 9: Slide loose belt to front of dryer and off drum by tilting drum upward. Slip on new belt the same way and position it over marks on drum left by old belt.

Step 10: With belt loose from idler, check idler pulley and bearings for damage. Remove idler pulley from shaft by removing the E-clip retaining ring.

Step 11: There are two bearings on either side of the pulley that have a slice through the side and a key that aligns with a slot inside the pulley. Bearings should be present and fit tightly. To remove or replace bearing, rotate until it goes into or out of position.

Step 12: Lubricate pulley shaft lightly with automotive type grease before reattaching idler pulley. Slide pulley back on shaft and reattach washers and retaining ring. Adjust retaining clip so pulley spins freely.

Belt and idler (continued)

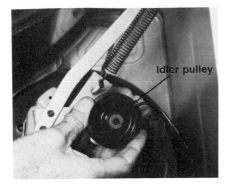

Step 13: If the idler pulley is cracked or broken, replace both pulley and bearing. Once pulley is reattached to shaft, rethread and align belt.

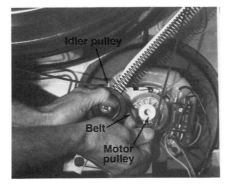

Step 14: To reattach belt to idler, rethread belt over top of idler pulley and underneath motor pulley. Release idler arm slowly. Check alignment on idler pulley by turning drum in both directions.

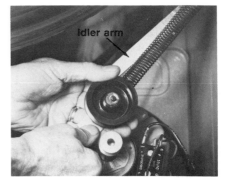

Step 15: If belt is positioned near front or rear edge of idler pulley, bend idler arm to center belt on idler pulley.

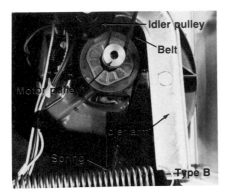

Step 16: Inspecting Type B. Examine each component in the idler assembly for visible damage. Check belt to see if it is worn, broken, or off of idler. If belt is off of idler, check spring for any breaks.

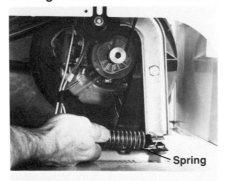

Step 17: If spring is broken, leave belt off of idler pulley and remove spring from tab on dryer base and bottom of idler arm. Hook new spring back into tab and idler arm.

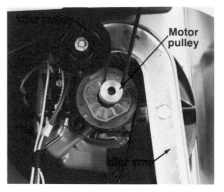

Step 18: If belt is securely in place and drum does not rotate, check to see if pulley on motor shaft will turn freely. If the motor shaft does not turn, check both motor and blower as described in Procedures #22 and #19.

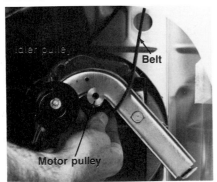

Step 19: If belt needs replacing, make sure it is first off of idler pulley. Swing idler arm away from pulleys, and belt should pop off. CAUTION: Be careful arm does not snap back on your hand. Reinstall belt as described in Steps 8 and 9.

Step 20: With belt loose from idler, check idler pulley and bearings as described in Steps 10-13.

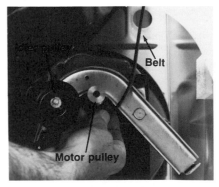

Step 21: To reattach belt to idler, rethread belt over idler pulley and underneath motor pulley. Release idler arm slowly. Check alignment on idler pulley by turning drum in both directions.

Belt and idler (continued)

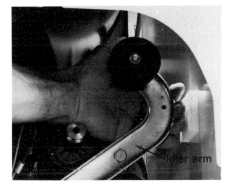

Step 22: If belt is positioned near front or rear edge of idler pulley, bend idler arm as shown to center belt on idler pulley.

Step 23: <u>Inspecting Type C.</u> Examine each component in the idler assembly for visible damage. Check belt to see if it is worn, broken, or off of idler.

Step 24: If belt is securely in place and drum does not rotate, check to see if pulley on motor shaft will turn freely. If the motor shaft does not turn, check both the motor and blower as described in Procedures #22 and #19.

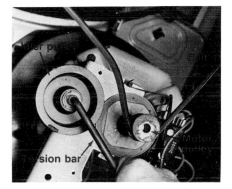

Step 25: If belt needs replacing, make sure it is off of idler pulley. Swing torsion bar down, and belt should pop off. **CAUTION:** Be careful bar does not snap back on your hand. Replace belt as described in Steps 8 and 9.

Step 26: With belt loose from idler, check idler pulley and bearings for damage. To access pulley, remove torsion bar mounting screws from dryer base. Lift off torsion bar and pulley.

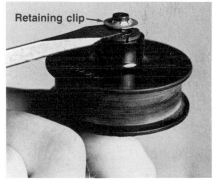

Step 27: Remove pulley retaining clip with screwdriver or needle-nose pliers, being careful not to damage clip. Check bearings as described in Step 11.

Step 28: Lubricate torsion bar shaft with automotive type grease at end that attaches to pulley. Reattach idler pulley. Slide pulley onto shaft and reattach retaining clip, adjusting so that pulley spins freely.

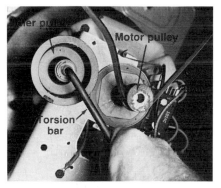

Step 29: To reattach belt to idler, pull torsion bar down. Rethread belt underneath motor pulley and over top of idler pulley. Release torsion bar slowly.

Step 30: Reassemble dryer and reconnect power supply.

Procedure 21
Inspecting and replacing centrifugal switch

Skill Level Rating: | Easy | Average | **Difficult** | Very Difficult |

The centrifugal switch is located on the rear of the motor. It closes the circuit to the start winding when the dryer is first started to give the motor starting power. At the same time, the centrifugal switch prevents electricity from reaching the heaters until the drum is turning and the blower is circulating air. Once the motor reaches top speed, certain contacts inside the centrifugal switch open to remove the start winding from the circuit, while other contacts close to energize the heating system.

A defective centrifugal switch can cause many dryer problems. The motor may simply not start, or it may hum if the start winding is not engaged. If the centrifugal contacts leading to the heating system are defective, the dryer will not heat.

There are three types of centrigual switches – one associated with each type of motor that has been used (T, V, or R). If only the switch is bad, you can replace it individually. Take the old switch to your authorized local appliance parts dealer when ordering a new switch. Should you need to replace the motor, a new centrifugal switch will come attached. **Be sure to also purchase a motor pulley if installing a new motor.**

Note: Your idler system may look different from the one pictured in this procedure, but the centrifugal switch is located, tested, and replaced the same way. In the photos below, note that the R and V switches have terminals on both sides. Be sure to reconnect wire leads to the correct terminals.

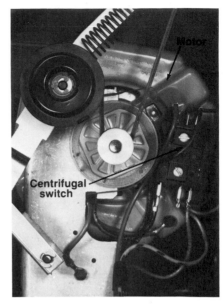

Centrifugal switch location

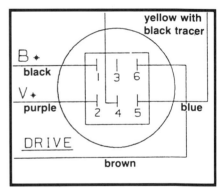

Switch wiring – electric dryer

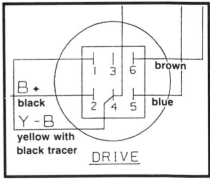

Switch wiring – gas dryer

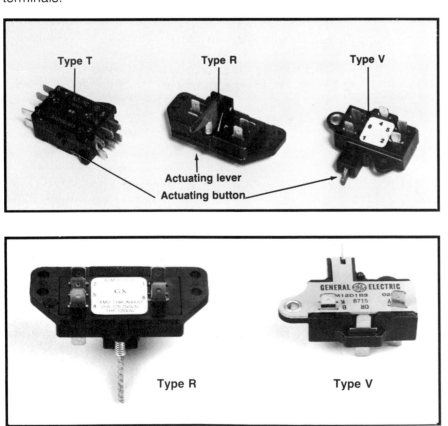

Centrifugal switch (continued)

Step 1: Be sure all dryer controls are turned **OFF**. Disconnect power supply at distribution panel, and unplug dryer from receptacle. Watch for sharp edges on access panels and parts.

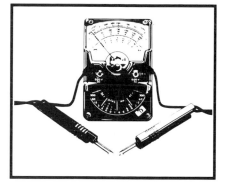

Step 2: This procedure requires the use of an ohmmeter. For instructions on how to use an ohmmeter, please refer to Tools and Testing Equipment, page 89.

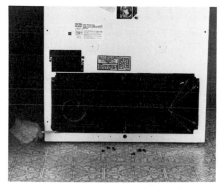

Step 3: Remove large, lower rear access panel by unscrewing mounting screws around cabinet.

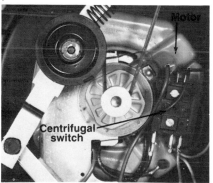

Step 4: The centrifugal switch is located on end of motor near its rear support.

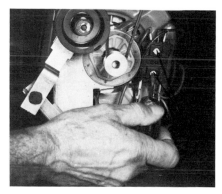

Step 5: Remove 2 mounting screws holding centrifugal switch to motor so that switch can be tested freely. For installation reference, make note of how all wires are connected as you remove them.

Step 6: Place ohmmeter probes across M1-M2. Meter should show continuity at R x 1 setting. Depress actuating button or lever, and needle should fall downscale and show no continuity.

Step 7: Place ohmmeter probes across M5-M6. Meter should show continuity at R x 1 setting. Depress actuating button or lever, and needle should fall downscale and show no continuity.

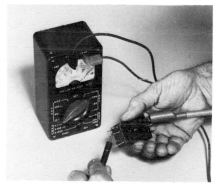

Step 8: Place ohmmeter probes across M5-M3. Meter should show no continuity at R x 1 setting. Depress actuating button or lever, and needle should sweep upscale to denote continuity.

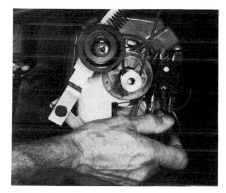

Step 9: Replace switch if it fails any of above tests. Connect all wire leads to new centrifugal switch and attach switch onto motor. Reassemble dryer and reconnect power supply.

Inspecting and replacing motor

Skill Level Rating: | Easy | Average | Difficult | **Very Difficult** |

The front motor shaft drives the blower, and the rear motor shaft drives the drum via a belt connected to a pulley system. The motor is located in the bottom of the dryer on the left side. For the motor to run, the door switch, timer, and start switch must be closed, and the centrifugal switch operational.

Several problems can occur with the motor. The start or run winding may open. If either winding is open, the motor will hum. The bearings may also wear out, which will bind the motor shaft. If any of these problems affect your motor, it must be replaced.

There are three types of motors used in dryers – types T, V, and R. They are all interchangeable and come with their own centrifugal switch. Unless your motor pulley is removable from your old motor, you will have to purchase a new pulley when you purchase the new motor.

Note: If dryer stops during cycle, wait ten minutes and start dryer again. If dryer starts, motor was overheating. Check for lint blockage around motor and for possible overloading. If dryer repeatedly stops during cycle, especially in the second of consecutive loads, replace motor.

Motor location (drum removed)

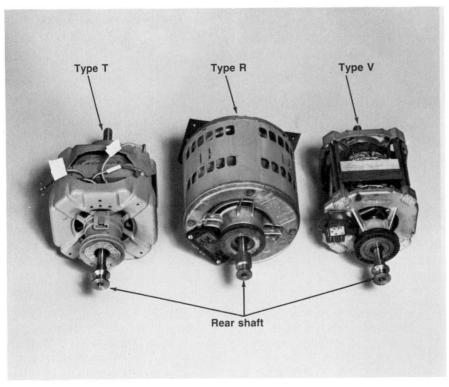

Various dryer motors

Motor (continued)

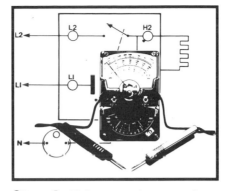

Step 1: Be sure all dryer controls are turned **OFF**. Disconnect power supply at distribution panel and unplug dryer from receptacle. Watch for sharp edges on access panels and parts.

Step 2: This procedure requires the use of an ohmmeter and ability to read a circuit diagram. For instructions, refer to Tools and Testing Equipment, pages 89-92.

Step 3: Remove large, lower rear access panel by unscrewing 5/16″ mounting screws around cabinet with nutdriver. Vacuum out any lint accumulation around motor.

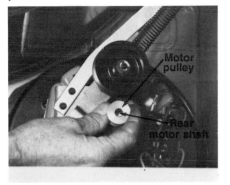

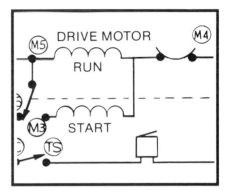

Step 4: Check rear motor shaft to see if it turns freely. If shaft does not turn, check blower wheel as described in Procedure #19: Inspecting and Replacing Blower Wheel. If blower is free from obstruction, but shaft will still not turn, replace motor.

Step 5: The idler assembly at the back of your motor may look different than the one pictured in the procedure. Location, testing, and replacement of the motor is the same, however.

Step 6: Locate motor contacts on your circuit diagram. On most dryers, M4-M5 energizes run winding, and M4-M3 energizes start winding.

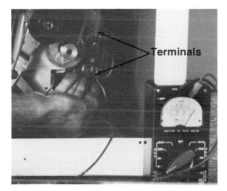

Step 7: Locate terminals corresponding to motor contacts that energize start winding on centrifugal switch. Remove one of wire leads.

Step 8: Place ohmmeter probes across terminals. Set on R x 1 scale, meter should move partially upscale. Repeat Steps 7 and 8 for terminals energizing run winding.

Step 9: If ohmmeter shows no upscale reading at either test, replace motor. To replace motor, remove drum. If you are unfamiliar with this process, please refer to Procedure #12: Removing Drum.

Motor (continued)

Step 10: To easily access motor, remove blower housing, motor, and idler from dryer base. First, remove 5/16" mounting screws attaching blower housing to cabinet front with nutdriver. Remove mounting screw to disconnect blower housing from ductwork.

Step 11: On models with a torsion bar idler system, you will need to release bar from dryer base by removing two mounting screws with nutdriver.

Step 12: Use wrench to remove two mounting nuts on rear motor support. For installation reference, make note of how wires are connected to centrifugal switch. Remove wire leads and move blower-motor-idler assembly outside of dryer for easy access.

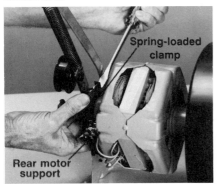

Step 13: To release motor from rear motor support, pry open spring-loaded clamp with screwdriver. **CAUTION:** Be careful not to place your finger where clamp can pinch. Remove ground strap from motor.

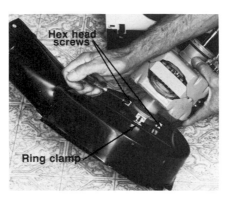

Step 14: To release front motor shaft from blower, loosen blower wheel clamp screw as shown in Step 10 of Procedure #19: Inspecting and Replacing Blower Wheel. Remove two screws holding ring clamp at front motor support with nutdriver.

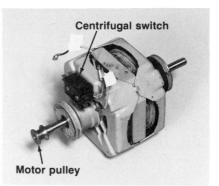

Step 15: New motor will have centrifugal switch attached, but will require attachment of motor pulley to rear shaft. Motor pulley from old motor may be used if there is a set screw to remove it from shaft.

Step 16: If motor pulley is nonremovable, purchase new motor pulley with your motor. To attach motor pulley to shaft of new motor, align set screw over hole and tighten with Allen wrench.

Step 17: Attach new motor to rear motor support using spring-loaded clamp removed in Step 13.

Step 18: Fit front motor mount through ring clamp at blower rear and tighten two screws. Reattach blower wheel clamp to front motor shaft but do not tighten.

Motor (continued)

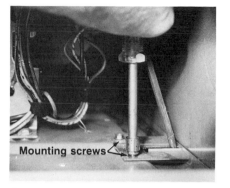

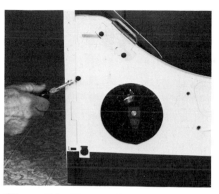

Step 19: Reattach motor to base of dryer, making sure that blower-motor-idler assembly is properly aligned. Reconnect wires to centrifugal switch.

Step 20: If your idler assembly has a torsion bar, reattach it to dryer base.

Step 21: Reattach screws to blower housing. Once you have made sure that blower wheel turns freely, tighten blower clamp. Reassemble dryer and reconnect power supply.

Inspecting and replacing drum supports

Skill Level Rating: | Easy | Average | **Difficult** | Very Difficult

The drum is supported two ways in a dryer--on the back drum shaft by a drum bearing, and on the front cabinet by two drum slide assemblies. Both the bearing and slide assemblies allow the drum to revolve smoothly. If bearing breaks, or the slides become loose and worn, the drum would move about too freely and make excessive noise.

Drum bearing located on rear drum shaft

New style drum bearing

Old style split drum bearing

Drum slide assembly located on dryer front cabinet

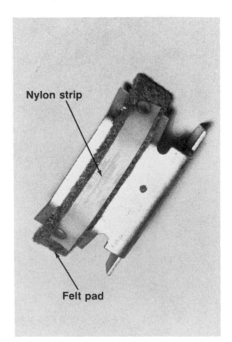

Nylon strip

Felt pad

Drum slide assembly

Drum supports (continued)

Step 1: Be sure all dryer controls are turned **OFF**. Disconnect power supply at distribution panel and unplug dryer from receptacle. Watch for sharp edges on access panels and parts.

Step 2: To inspect drum slides, raise the dryer top and remove dryer front. If you are unfamiliar with this process, refer to Procedure #5: Removing Access and Control Panels.

Step 3: Inspect slides for worn and broken areas. If slides are damaged, replace. Use nutdriver to remove slide mounting screws.

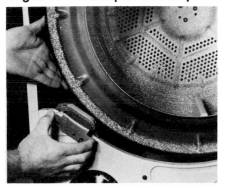

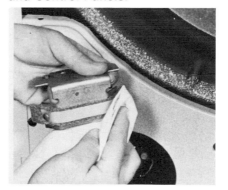

Step 4: Hold dryer drum in place to keep drum from falling onto dryer cabinet, then lift drum slide out from mounting location. Let dryer drum down, to rest on dryer cabinet.

Step 5: Before mounting new drum slide, use a clean cloth to apply a few drops of a special silicone oil (available from your authorized local appliance parts dealer) to nylon strip and felt pad. Reattach mounting screws to secure slide to cabinet.

Step 6: To access drum bearing assembly, remove drum. If you are unfamiliar with the process, refer to Procedure #12: Removing Drum.

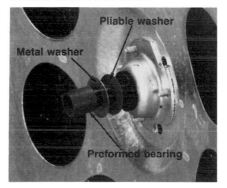

Step 7: After the drum is removed, check bearing on rear shaft or inside rear housing in dryer cabinet. If it is worn or broken, slip a new bearing onto the rear shaft. No lubrication is necessary for this bearing.

Step 8: Look for two washers on drum shaft. These washers may have fallen off when drum was removed. Check to see that the pliable washer is on shaft first, followed by metal washer.

Step 9: Be sure when you reinsert the drum into dryer that bearing and washers do not fall off rear shaft, and that bearing is not pushed out back of bearing retainer. Reassemble dryer and reconnect power supply.

Adjusting dryer door

Skill Level Rating: | Easy | **Average** | Difficult | Very Difficult

If the dryer door is not properly aligned with the front of the dryer, the door may not close, or it may rub and scratch the dryer cabinet as it closes. A misaligned door can also affect dryer air flow and cause the dryer to overheat.

There are differences in how doors on various models are hinged and therefore in how the doors can be adjusted. Certain models can only be adjusted at the upper hinge inside the dryer top. Others can be adjusted at both the upper and lower hinges inside the door.

Door needing alignment

Step 1: Be sure all dryer controls are turned **OFF**. Disconnect power supply at distribution panel and unplug dryer from receptacle. Watch for sharp edges on access panels.

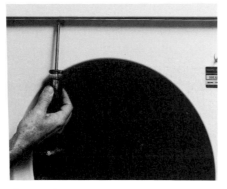

Step 2: To access upper hinge on standard capacity dryers and newer large capacity dryers, raise dryer top. If you are unfamiliar with this process, please refer to Procedure #5: Removing Access and Control Panels.

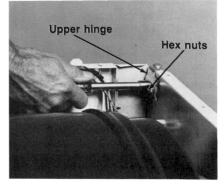

Step 3: The upper hinge of these models is located inside front right-hand corner underneath top. To loosen door for adjustment, loosen two hex nuts on hinge.

Step 4: Move door around until it aligns with dryer front and tighten hex nuts. Make adjustments several times, if necessary, until door aligns properly with dryer cabinet.

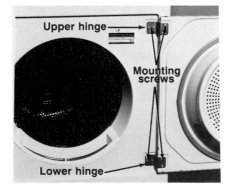

Step 5: Door hinges on earlier large capacity dryer models are located on right-hand side inside door. Mounting screws on both sides of hinge can be loosened for adjustment.

Step 6: Move door around until it aligns with dryer front and tighten screws, being careful not to overtighten. Make adjustment several times, if necessary, until door aligns properly with dryer cabinet.

Procedure 25
Inspecting and replacing door latch assembly

Skill Level Rating:	Easy	**Average**	Difficult	Very Difficult

The door latch assembly has two parts. The "strike" is a prong-like object extending from the dryer door liner. When the door closes, the strike engages the "catch", mounted in the front of the dryer. If the strike does not enter the catch at the right position, try to realign the door, as described in Procedure #24: Adjusting Dryer Door. If either part has been damaged or appears worn, replace both the strike and the catch.

Note: Replacement catches are now plastic. If your dryer has a metal catch housed in a long rectangular adapter plate that screws to the dryer front, you will need a new adapter plate or "C" clip to attach the new latch. If your metal latch was housed in an unfastened chrome trim, simply insert the new plastic latch without modification.

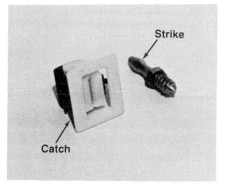

Replacement assembly

Step 1: For your personal safety, exercise caution when working with any electrical appliance. Be sure to put a protective coating over the jaws of your pliers to prevent damage to dryer cabinet.

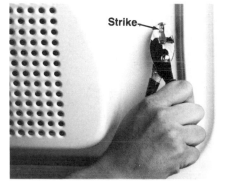

Step 2: To replace a defective strike, grip it with a pair of pliers or wrench. Unscrew strike from door liner. Replace new strike by screwing it into position.

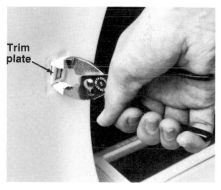

Step 3: To remove a defective metal catch, grip its edges inside chrome trim with a pair of pliers and pull gently out. Some catches are mounted in an adapter plate that is attached to the front with two screws. Remove this plate prior to removing catch.

Step 4: If catch is plastic, remove it by raising dryer top and squeezing side tabs from inside dryer. Replace new catch by simply pressing in from the front.

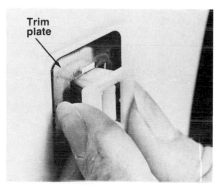

Step 5: If dryer had a metal catch and trim plate, attach trim plate to new catch and press into dryer front. Discard rectangular "C" clip that may come with replacement part.

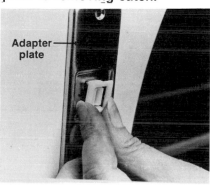

Step 6: If dryer had a metal catch and adapter plate, your new part will either have a new adapter plate or "C" clip to secure latch. Press new catch into new adapter plate and attach to dryer front, or use the rectangular "C" clip to secure latch to old plate. "C" clip must go behind 2 ears on back of plastic catch.

Procedure 26
Inspecting and replacing door switch/dryer light

Skill Level Rating: | Easy | Average | **Difficult** | Very Difficult |

The door switch prevents the dryer from running when the door is open. The switch is located on the upper right-hand side of the dryer front inside the door. As the door closes, the depressed switch completes the electrical circuit necessary for dryer operation. Some models have a light, located at the top of the front opening into the drum, that comes on when the door is open. The door switch on these models has three terminals, of which two of the contacts will be alternatively closed.

If the dryer does not run, or new light bulbs will not work, the contacts in the door switch may be defective and should be checked with an ohmmeter.

Door switch and light location

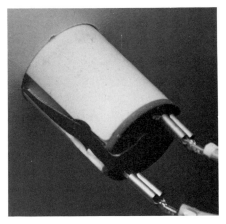

Internal wiring to switch

Step 1: Be sure all dryer controls are turned **OFF**. Disconnect power supply at distribution panel and unplug dryer from receptacle. Watch for sharp edges on access panels.

Step 2: This procedure requires the use of an ohmmeter. For instructions, refer to Tools and Testing Equipment, page 89.

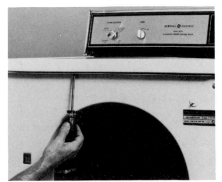

Step 3: Raise dryer top. If you are unfamiliar with this process, refer to Procedure #5: Removing Access and Control Panels.

Door switch/dryer light (continued)

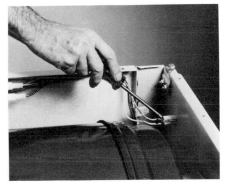

Step 4: When dryer top is raised, door switch is easily accessed inside upper right-hand side.

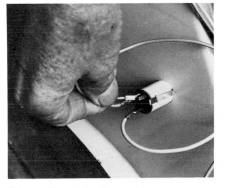

Step 5: To test switch connections to motor, remove wire leads from both terminals on 2-terminal switch. On 3-terminal switch, remove wire leads to the 2 smaller terminals.

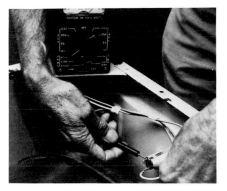

Step 6: Place ohmmeter probes across the 2 exposed terminals. Depress door switch on dryer front and test for continuity with ohmmeter set on R x 1 scale. If no continuity, replace switch.

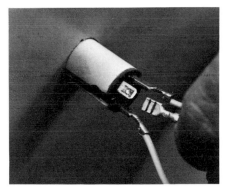

Step 7: With wire leads still removed from the two smaller terminals, remove wire lead from remaining terminal to test dryer light connection. Open dryer door.

Step 8: Place probes across largest terminal and sequentially to each of the smaller terminals. On R x 1 scale, ohmmeter should show continuity across one but not both of the smaller terminals. If no continuity at either terminal, replace switch.

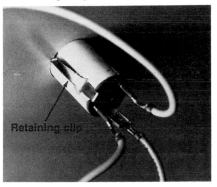

Step 9: To remove switch on some models, squeeze together two retaining clips that mount switch. On other models, there is a mounting nut that is unscrewed.

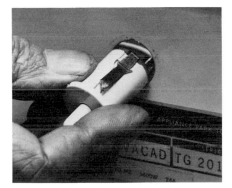

Step 10: Once you have loosened switch, pull it through dryer front. Insert new switch through dryer front and snap retaining clips into position or reattach mounting nut. Reconnect wires.

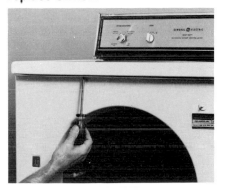

Step 11: Reassemble dryer and reconnect power supply.

Procedure 27
Cosmetic repairs

Skill Level Rating:	Easy	Average	Difficult	Very Difficult

You can help keep the appearance of your dryer in "showroom" condition by following maintenance instructions in your *Use and Care Book* or in the preventive maintenance section of this manual (page 86). Properly applying a coat of appliance polish at least twice a year will also help your appliance maintain a new look and provide protection against rust.

Over the years, through accidents or moving, you may encounter problems that require more extensive repairs. Handles, nameplates, trim and cabinet panels can usually be replaced. Painted cabinet bodies can be touched up with spray paint or touch-up pencils. Porcelain enamel surfaces are difficult to repair. Although there are porcelain repair kits available, the recommended procedure is to replace the damaged part or panel. These products are usually available through your authorized local appliance parts dealer.

Note: Be sure to use the complete and correct model identification number when purchasing parts or paint.

CAUTION: Paint is flammable. Always paint in a well-ventilated area away from open flame. Read all instructions on paint container carefully. Do not allow paint to contact plastic surfaces.

Matching touch-up paint is available for repairing scratches

Cosmetics (continued)

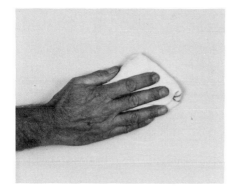

Step 1: For your personal safety, exercise caution when working with any electrical appliance. Watch for sharp edges on trim. Spray paint in well-ventilated area away from flame.

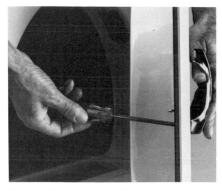

Step 2: Damaged trim is replaced by removing retaining screws. When removing or attaching trim, use care not to overtighten screws that attach trim to painted or porcelain finish. Overtightening screws can chip or scratch finish.

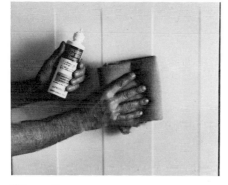

Step 3: To remove soil, wash cabinet with a liquid household detergent and warm water. Remove all traces of wax with a wax remover. Rinse with clear water.

Step 4: To repair small scratches, spray small amount of paint into top of can and apply with a torn match, or use touch-up paint kit with brush applicator. Use paint sparingly to fill scratch.

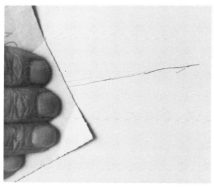

Step 5: Sand large scratches smooth with extra-fine sandpaper. Sand scratch until edge is "feathered" smoothly into exposed metal. Area to be painted must be clean, dry, and free of grease or rust.

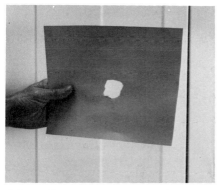

Step 6: Practice with spray paint before applying primer coat to dryer. Read and follow instructions on paint can. Do not aim paint directly at damaged area. Spray area through an irregular hole in a piece of paper.

Step 7: Spray paint through paper hole as you sweep across scratch. This practice allows paint to blend with original coat without obvious lines. Do not apply too much paint as it will run and sag.

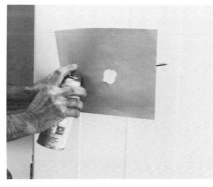

Step 8: After primer coat has dried, sand lightly and spray again with matching appliance finish coat. Be sure to read all instructions on can carefully.

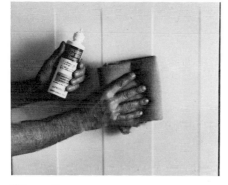

Step 9: Allow finish coat to dry and rewax with appliance polish. Be careful not to allow paint to come into contact with plastic surfaces.

Technical assistance/Service record

This page is provided a a convenient reference of important dryer repair information. There are spaces for you to record your dryer model number, parts needed, repair notes (such as where wire leads reattach), and when repairs were made. There are also spaces for you to write down the phone numbers of your nearest GE/Hotpoint parts dealer and Factory Service Center.

Another important phone number for repair information belongs to the GE Answer Center® consumer information service. If you have difficulty making any repair described in this book you can contact the GE Answer Center® consumer information service by calling 800-626-2000 toll free. The trained service professionals will try to talk you through the problem step. It helps to write down your model number, what you have done, and what is causing you difficulty before calling.

Model number: _____

Parts or components needed:

_____

_____

Repair notes:

_____

_____

Service record:

_____

_____

Fuse or circuit breaker location: _____

Size fuse required: _____ (30 amp for electric dryer; 15-20 amp for gas dryer) _____

Phone number of GE/Hotpoint parts dealer: _____

Phone number of GE/Hotpoint Factory Service Center: _____

Preventive maintenance

At GE, we're committed to your satisfaction. The basic do's and don'ts included in this section are our way of helping you obtain the best results from your GE/Hotpoint dryer. The few minutes that you invest in caring for your dryer properly can save you a great deal of time and trouble.

This section outlines basic precautions and simple maintenance routines that will help prevent the small problems that can lead to big repair jobs. Take a little time to read this part of the manual and to follow the advice given.

Dryer exterior maintenance

- Never permit anyone to climb or stand on the dryer; damage or injury could result.
- Wipe off any spilled laundry compounds as soon as possible using a damp cloth. Keep stain remover or presoak products away from your dryer as these can damage outside surfaces.
- Do not use harsh or gritty cleaners. Clean control panel with a glass cleaner or a damp soft cloth.
- Keep sharp objects away from the surface.
- The ductwork should be arranged in the shortest and straightest path to the outside vent. Refer to the installation instructions that come with your dryer for proper venting.

Dryer interior maintenance

- Remove and clean the lint filter after each use.
- Remove the service panels yearly and vacuum any lint accumulation, especially around the heater housing and motor.
- Check the dryer vent periodically to remove any lint accumulation.

Improving the performance of your dryer

- Refer to the **Use and Care Book** for proper operation of your dryer.
- Do not overload your dryer. Allow more space to dry permanent press loads than for cottons and linens.
- Sort loads by fabric, weight and color.
- Use heat settings according to fabric type as recommended in the **Use and Care Book**.
- Read garment label for drying instructions.
- To avoid wrinkling, remove clothes from dryer and place on hangers immediately after dryer stops tumbling. Wrinkles are often not removed in the dryer from clothes that were overloaded in the washer.

Tools and testing equipment

Tools

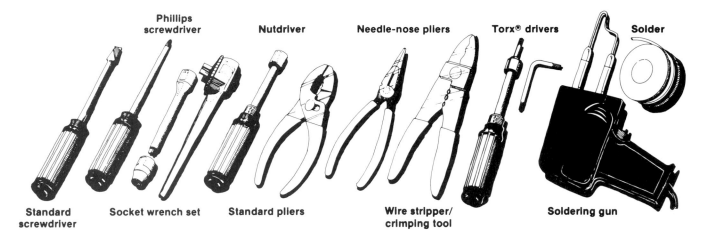

Phillips screwdriver · Nutdriver · Needle-nose pliers · Torx® drivers · Solder

Standard screwdriver · Socket wrench set · Standard pliers · Wire stripper/ crimping tool · Soldering gun

Chances are you already have some of the above tools in your home. For safety and efficiency reasons it is important to use the proper tools when making dryer repairs.

The tool you will use the most is the 5/16″ nutdriver. The nutdriver is made like a screw-driver but has a small socket on one end. This socket fits over the hexagon head of the screw or nut. It's used just like a screw-driver.

The socket wrench usually has a handle with a rachet that can be set to tighten or loosen a nut, an extension, and various sockets.

Sockets usually come in a set containing several sizes, and there are several sizes of nuts used with the dryer.

To use a socket wrench, place the socket on the nut and turn the handle counter-clockwise to loosen it. If it makes a clicking sound and does not turn, flip the rachet lever to the opposite direction and loosen the nut.

Testing equipment

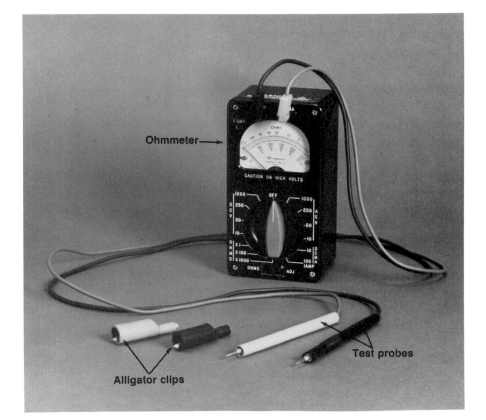

Ohmmeter

Alligator clips · Test probes

Ohmmeter

Testing equipment

An ohmmeter is required to diagnose the workings of the electrical components of your dryer. The ohmmeter is a simple device that measures the amount of resistance in an electrical circuit. Ohmmeters are usually combined with a voltmeter into an instrument called a multimeter, multitester, or volt-ohmmeters (VOM). Volt-ohmmeters can measure the amount of both resistance and voltage in an electrical circuit. A simple, inexpensive ohmmeter will be sufficient for any dryer repairs presented in this manual.

Most problems that occur in an electrical circuit are invisible. For example, it is difficult to see contacts that are not closing inside its insulation. For the most part, you'll be using the ohmmeter only as a continuity tester to determine whether or not current can pass through the circuit. By passing a small electrical current from a battery contained inside the ohmmeter through the circuit, you can tell if the circuit is complete.

To understand the basic flow of electricity, think of it in terms of a water pumping station. In order for water to flow through the pipes, it must have a complete "closed loop" from the pump, through the valves, then back to the pump again. If the

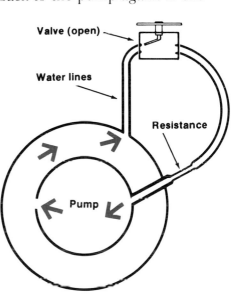

line is broken or opened at any point, water would eventually cease to flow.

The flow of electricity through your dryer is similar to the pumping of water, except electrons rather than water are flowing through the dryer circuitry. The pump is the dryer plug-in receptacle that provides the force to circulate current through the dryer circuits. The electrical circuit uses wires rather than pipes as the

conductors of electricity and switches rather than valves to control the flow. Voltage corresponds to the pressure that exists in a water circuit, whereas electrical current could be compared to the flow rate of water that flows through the pipe.

Some tests with an ohmmeter will be needed for repair procedures presented in this manual. An ohmmeter will have either a switch or pair of jacks (plugs) that allow you to select the function of the meter. Resistance is measured in units called ohms and will be designated by the symbol Ω or

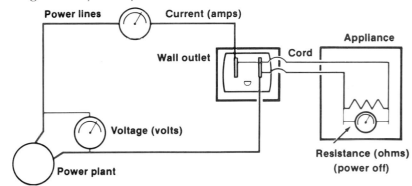

the letter R. Your meter may have more than one range scale. When set at R × 1, the reading should be taken directly from the meter. When set at a higher scale, such as R × 100, the reading on the scale should be multiplied by 100 to obtain the correct resistance. Most measurements for testing components or circuits are made on the lowest scale, usually R × 1. Some newer digital ohmmeters do not use a multiplier and have only high, medium, and low ranges.

Plug the test leads in the jacks marked "ohms". The red lead goes in the positive (+) jack and the black on to negative (−). If your meter gives you a choice of functions, select the range first, then "zero" the meter by

touching the two test probes together. With the probes tightly in contact with each other, the needle of the meter should sweep towards "O" (zero) resistance. Now, while holding the probes together, adjust the knob marked "zero adjust" or "ohms adjust" until the needle rests directly over "O".

At this point, you can see exactly how the meter works. If instead of touching the probes together you touch them to each end of a wire, or to a fuse, the needle should sweep toward "O". This indicates that the wire or fuse will conduct electricity.

But if the wire or fuse is broken inside, the needle would not move. When this condition exists in a component or circuit, it is said to be "open", and it cannot conduct electricity. But if the needle moves to indicate that it does conduct electricity, then the component or circuit is said to have "continuity".

All wires in the electrical circuit should indicate "O" resistance when tested in this manner. Switches should indicate "O" resistance when they're turned on, and should be open when turned off. Components that do work will offer some electrical resistance, but will not be open. The meter reading for these instances should be somewhere between full scale and no reading.

Tools and testing equipment (continued)

Many repair procedures in this manual advise you to test for grounds when checking a component. When doing this, you should select the highest resistance scale on the ohmmeter. You will be directed to place one test probe on a terminal of the component and the other test probe on a metallic portion of the component housing. No current should flow throuth those paths; if the meter indicates that continuity exists under those conditions, the component is grounded and should be replaced.

The repair procedures in this manual will show you the test points (where to place the test probes) for various tests. You'll find an ohmmeter to be a valuable addition to your home tool collection. For further information on the function and operation of the ohmmeter, see pages 87 and 88.

Using the ohmmeter

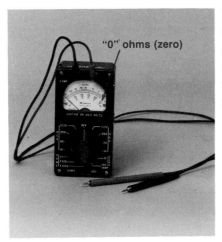

"0" ohms (zero)

Full-featured ohmmeters like this one shown have numerous switch-selected ranges. Note that ohms scale at top is reversed — zero resistance is at full sweep of scale.

Inexpensive ohmmeters use jacks rather than switches to select function, but still provide zero ohms adjustment. Note that red lead plugs into positive (+) jack, black into negative (−) or common.

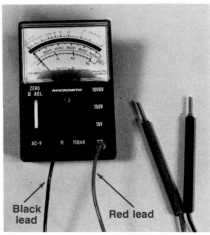

Black lead

Red lead

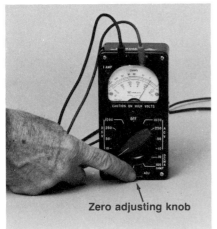

Zero adjusting knob

To zero ohmmeter, touch probes tightly together, turn zero adjustment knob until needle is centered over "O" (ZERO) at full sweep of scale. This adjusts readout to the battery condition and to the resistance selected.

Sometimes you can't identify a blown fuse, even when it has a glass shell. Saving a single service call for a simple problem like this can pay for the price of a meter.

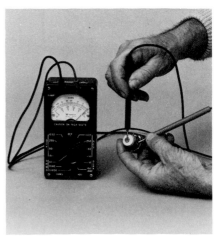

CAUTION: Do not attempt to test resistance of any circuit with the power turned on. Checking a live voltage circuit will damage your testing meter.

How to interpret circuit diagrams

The circuit diagram (schematic) that accompanies your dryer shows how wiring is connected between components, and how the internal electrical circuitry is arranged. The secret to using a circuit diagram is to simplify the diagram. When reading a diagram, focus your attention only on that part of the diagram that involves the area you are testing. (Relevant symbols and abbreviations are listed at the end of this section.)

Circuit diagrams may be drawn in several different ways. Some component symbols may be different, but all show the path of current flow from the lines through the switches and components. This flow of current depicts the continuous loop required to complete an electrical circuit.

For explanation purposes, let's study the circuit diagram of a typical electric dryer in the "ON" position. Electricity flows between L1 and L2 (240 volts) through the heaters and their control circuits; 120 volts flow between L1 and N through the drive motor circuit.

When the machine is first started, centrifugal switch contacts, M1-M2 and M5-M6, are open, and M5-M3 are closed. When the start switch (W1-W5) is depressed, the start and run windings of the drive motor are energized.

Centrifugal switch contacts, M1-M2, stay open until the motor reaches top speed to prevent electricity from reaching the heat source until the drum is turning and the blower is circulating air. The spinning force of the motor changes these centrifugal switch contacts, M5-M3 to M5-

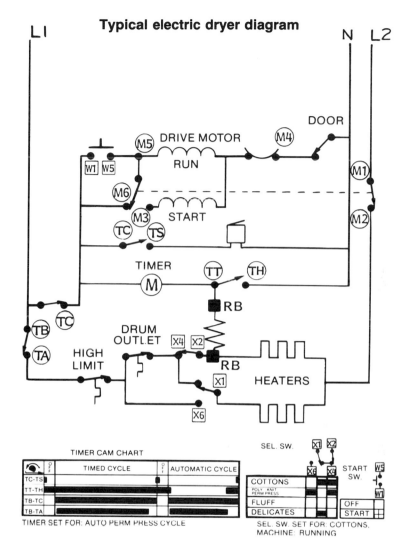

Typical electric dryer diagram

TIMER CAM CHART

TIMER SET FOR: AUTO PERM PRESS CYCLE

SEL. SW. SET FOR: COTTONS.
MACHINE: RUNNING

M6 (removing the start winding) and closes M1-M2 (energizing the heaters). The timer, thermostat, and selector switches control the amount of heat generated by the heaters.

The drum outlet thermostat is sensitive to the temperature of the air as it flows out of the drum. When the temperature reaches the trip point, the drum outlet thermostat opens to shut down the heater. As the dryer cools down, the drum outlet thermostat will reset or close so that electricity can once again energize the heaters. The high limit thermostat acts as a safety switch should the air in the dryer become overheated due

to a malfunction or insufficient airflow. It is set to open at a higher temperature than the drum outlet thermostat.

The fabric type or temperature selection is set on the selector switches. As seen in the selector switch chart for the electric dryer, contacts, X1-X4 and X2-X4, are closed for the cotton cycle, energizing both heaters for high high heat. During the fluff or air only cycle, all of the selector switches are open, shutting down both heaters. For delicate fabrics only X1-X4 is closed, operating one heater and supplying low heat.

Tools and testing equipment (continued)

When the timed cycle is selected, the timer motor will run for the desired amount of time. Contacts TB-TA, TB-TC, and TT-TH are closed. When the cycle ends, TB-TA opens first to shut down the heaters, and then TB-TC opens to shut down the drive motor.

During the automatic cycle, the timer runs when the heat is off. For the automatic cycle, TT-TH remains open for most of the cycle. The resistor and timer motor provide a higher resistance over that part of the circuit, and electricity will preferentially flow through the thermostats rather than through the timer. Once the thermostat opens, however, electricity flows through the resistor and the timer motor.

Because the resistor and the timer motor have approximately the same resistance, they divide the voltage equally, so that the timer motor runs on 120-V rather than 240-V. Prior to the end of the cycle, TB-TA opens to shut off the heat, and TT-TH closes to run the timer motor and allow for an 8-10 minute cool down.

The motor and timer circuit for a gas dryer resembles that observed in the electric dryer schematic. The centrifugal switch contacts operate in exactly the same manner. Electrical power for the gas dryer, however, comes from a 120-V line rather than a 240-V line. Because the heat comes from a gas burner rather than electric heaters, the energizing of the heat source and the thermostat system is also different.

Three circuits are completed to turn on the heat. One path is through the detector, igniter,

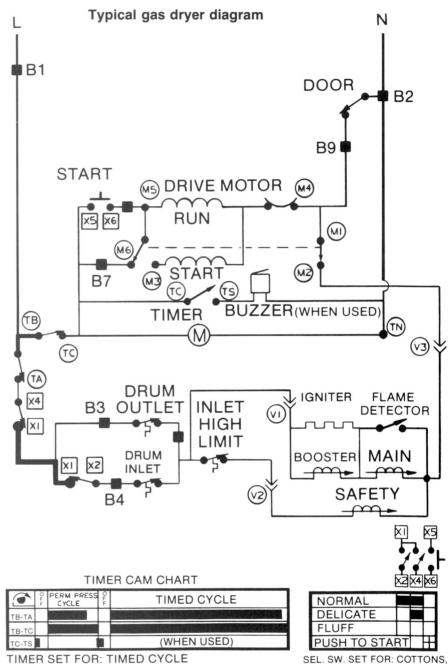

Typical gas dryer diagram

	OFF	PERM PRESS CYCLE	OFF	TIMED CYCLE
TB-TA				
TB-TC				
TC-TS				(WHEN USED)

TIMER CAM CHART

TIMER SET FOR: TIMED CYCLE

NORMAL			
DELICATE			
FLUFF			
PUSH TO START			

SEL. SW. SET FOR: COTTONS,
MACHINE: RUNNING

and thermostats. Another path is through the detector, booster coil, and thermostat. The third path is through the safety coil and thermostats. When the booster and safety coils are energized, the safety valve is opened electromagnetically to start the gas flow. As the igniter becomes hot enough to ignite the gas, the flame detector (sensitive to a specific temperature) opens, routing

the current through the main coil.

The energizing of the main coil opens the main valve, allowing gas to pass through the ignition port where it is ignited. The flame detector now stays open from the heat of the flame. Once the main valve is energized, there is less voltage reaching the igniter and booster. The igniter cools down, but the function of the booster coil is not materially affected.

The drum inlet thermostat, situated close to the heat source, will open first when the air gets warm enough. To shut off the gas flame, the drum outlet thermostat must also be open. Once the drum outlet has opened, the drum inlet becomes the controlling thermostat. Because the drum inlet thermostat resets at a higher temperature than the drum outlet thermostat, the drum outlet thermostat will not have chance to reset. As with the electric dryer, the inlet high limit thermostat acts a a safety switch, should the other thermostat malfunction or there is insufficient airflow.

The selector switches, X1-X2 and X1-X4, control the current flow to the thermostats and thus regulate the amount of heat used for each cycle. When X1-X4 is open, the heat system cannot be energized, so no heat is supplied (fluff cycle). When X1-X2 is open, the drum inlet thermostat is removed from the circuit, and the drum outlet becomes the controlling thermostat. Because the drum outlet thermostat resets at a lower air temperature than the drum inlet thermostat, low heat is supplied as in the delicate cycle.

By learning to properly interpret circuit diagrams, you will have an insight into your dryer's electrical function. This insight should allow you to use your ohmmeter to pinpoint a problem quickly and accurately. Circuit diagrams are located in an envelope glued inside the backsplash control panel, or glued to the rear of the cabinet.

Symbols

The following Legend of Symbols and Abbreviations will assist you in reading the circuit diagrams.

BUZZER		SWITCH OR CONTACT	
HEATING UNIT		TERMINAL BOARD	
MOTOR		THERMOSTAT	
OVERLOAD PROTECTOR		WIRES CONNECTED	
RESISTOR		WIRES CROSSING	
SOLENOID OR MOTOR WINDING			

Abbreviations

B—TERMINAL BOARD

T—TIMER

X-SELECTOR SWITCH

V-GAS VALVE

Dryer accessories

In addition to supplying quality original replacement parts for your dryer, GE also provides a variety of useful home laundry accessories to keep your dryer looking and working like new. The most popular and widely available dryer accessories are featured below.

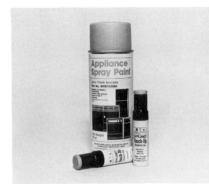

Appliance paint

High quality paints in spray cans and touch-up applicators are available in five colors to match GE/Hotpoint appliances. Camouflaging most nicks and scratches, GE appliance paint is an easy-to-use and long-lasting way to improve your dryer's appearance.

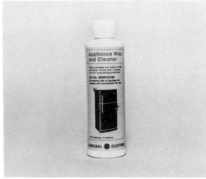

Appliance wax and cleaner

Protective liquid wax contains silicone sealant to clean, polish and wax in one easy step. The 8-oz. squeeze bottle contains enough liquid wax for several applications to keep your dryer finish in like-new condition.

WR97X216

Light bulbs

Replacement light bulbs for your dryer are available from GE. Bulbs are specifically designed to withstand high heat, and are supplied according to electrical specifications for GE/Hotpoint dryers.

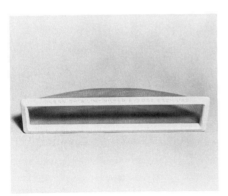

Lint filter

Renew your dryer's performance with a new lint filter. Long-lasting filter traps particles to help keep clothes lint free. Constructed of styrene and mesh, the lint filter is easy to clean and replace.

WE18X26R

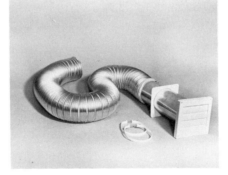

Exhaust vent

Aluminum exhaust duct and louvered vent allow for proper venting of gas or electric dryers. The fire-resistant, 4″ diameter, metallic duct is flexible and easy to install. The louvered vent cap opens to vent and closes when dryer is off to decrease drafts and save energy.

WX8X75A

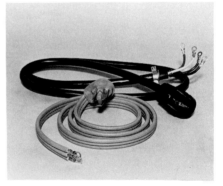

Power cord

Replacement power cords for electric dryers are available through GE. Designed specifically to electrical specifications for GE/Hotpoint dryers, power cords have eyelet connectors to simplify replacement.

WR97X216A

Glossary of terms

Advance
To move forward in a cycle.

Backsplash
Control housing on top of dryer.

Bearing
Device that supports, guides, and reduces friction between fixed and moving parts.

Bell connector
Solderless connector for splicing wiring. Insulating cover crimps onto ends of wires to assure solid connection.

Belt
Continuous band of flexible material that transfers motion or power from motor pulley to drum.

Cam chart
Chart showing which switches are opened and closed in timer at various points in drying cycle. A cam is a notched wheel mounted on a rotating shaft in timer. As it turns, it activates switches that regulate drying cycles.

Catch
Female portion of door latch assembly that secures door to dryer front when door is closed. See also STRIKE.

Centrifugal switch
A switch in the motor that disengages start winding and energizes heaters after motor reaches top speed.

Circuit
Path of electrical current from power supply through wiring to point of use and back to source.

Circuit breaker
Device to protect circuit from current overload. "Tripped" circuit breaker interrupts circuit when current exceeds specified amount. See also FUSE.

Circuit diagram
Drawing using standard symbols to represent path of current from power supply through switches and components and back to source. Shows how wiring is connected between components and how internal wiring of components is arranged.

Closed (circuit)
Complete circuit which can conduct electricity.

Combustion chamber
Enclosure behind gas valve assembly in gas dryers where the ignition of gas occurs.

Glossary of terms (continued)

Component
An individual electrical or mechanical part of a dryer system.

Contact
Switch component which opens and closes to complete or break an electrical circuit.

Continuity
Ability of completed circuit to conduct electricity.

Cycle
As a verb, to repeatedly turn components on and off. As a noun, a particular sequence of events that occurs in a given dryer selection.

Defective
In this manual, used to mean a component which does not function properly and which must be replaced.

Distribution panel
Fuse or circuit breaker box that distributes incoming power from outside line into a number of household circuits.

Drum
Rotating component of the dryer which contains the clothes load.

Energize
To supply electrical current for operation of a component.

Flame detector
Component of gas assembly that senses when gas flame has been lit and turns off igniter.

Fuse
Device to protect circuit from current overload. "Blown" fuse automatically interrupts circuit when current exceeds specified amount. See also CIRCUIT BREAKER.

Fuse block
Separate part of distribution panel that contains large fuses used for electric dryer circuit. Usually two cartridge-type fuses joined at the handle.

Gas valve & burner assembly
Components of a gas dryer that regulate flow and ignition of gas.

Ground
Connection to earth or to another conducting body which transmits current to earth. Metal components in a circuit must be grounded to prevent their accidentally becoming electrically charged, causing injury.

Housing
Plastic or metal casing that covers a component.

Idler assembly
A pulley system on a shaft that rests or presses against a drive belt. Also includes a torsion bar or a spring-loaded arm to maintain a specified tension on the drive belt.

Igniter
Part of gas valve and burner assembly that ignites gas.

Inoperative
In this manual, used to mean a component which does not function, but which can be checked and possibly repaired.

Lead
Portion of electrical wiring attached to component.

Nutdriver
Tool used to remove and reinstall hexagonal-head screws or nuts. Resembles a screwdriver with a small socket at the end instead of a blade.

Ohm
Measurement unit for electrical resistance.

Ohmmeter
Battery-operated test instrument for determining the continuity of a circuit and measuring its resistance.

Open (circuit)
Incomplete circuit which cannot conduct electricity.

Pulley
A wheel turned by or driving a belt.

Resistance
Restriction of current in an electrical circuit.

Resistor
Electrical component used to add resistance to a circuit.

Schematic
Another term for circuit diagram. See CIRCUIT DIAGRAM.

Short (circuit)
Accidentally created circuit between hot wire and any ground, allowing excessive current with little or no resistance.

Solenoid
Cylindrical coil of insulated wire that establishes a magnetic field in presence of current.

Strike
Male portion of door latch assembly that protrudes from inside of door. See also CATCH.

Glossary of terms (continued)

Switch
Device to turn current on and off in an electrical circuit.

Terminal
Connection point between wiring and electrical components. Commonly used terminals in dryers are push-on terminals, which are held in place by their snug fit.

Terminal block
Board on back of electric dryers for connecting power cord.

Terminal board
A board containing multiple electrical connections; in gas dryers where the wires for lower part of dryer meet those from upper part.

Test probes
Metal components of ohmmeter which are attached to either end of a circuit during testing for continuity or resistance. See also OHMMETER.

Thermostat
Heat-sensing component that controls temperature levels by turning heat source on and off.

Upscale
Reading from ohmmeter that indicates continuity in a circuit.

Volt
Measurement unit for electrical pressure.

Wall cap
Portion of dryer exhaust ductwork that passes through wall to outside.

Winding
One or more turns of wire forming a continuous coil for a relay or other rotating machine. A conductive path is formed by the wire.

Index

Index (continued)

Index (continued)